Calming
Dot-to-Dot

Calming
Dot-to-Dot

ARCTURUS

Arcturus

This edition published in 2018 by Arcturus Publishing Limited
26/27 Bickels Yard, 151–153 Bermondsey Street,
London SE1 3HA

ISBN: 978-1-78888-029-9
CH006357NT
Supplier 29, Date 0118, Print run 6780

Printed in China

Created for children 10+

Introduction

For many, dot-to-dot puzzles have an incredibly calming influence. By focusing on the simple task of joining one dot to the next, you can bring focus to your thoughts and relieve the tensions of a stressful mind.

This collection of dot-to-dot images is a great source of soothing, mindful activity to restore your sense of peace and calm. There are more than 150 to choose from and they range from everyday objects and scenes from nature to esoteric symbols. Each puzzle is made up of between 150 and 200 dots, so you'll be able to gradually unwind as you uncover each hidden image.

It's easy to get started, all you need is a pencil and an opportunity to sit down and start your drawing. Simply locate the first numbered dot and join it to the next one, in ascending order. The convenient size makes this book perfect for enjoying some calming dot-to-dots on the go.

We advise using a ruler to keep your hand steady and, if you feel inspired, you can always add decoration and embellishment to the finished drawing.

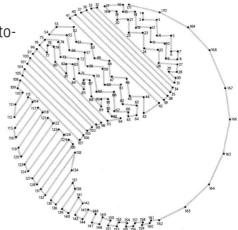

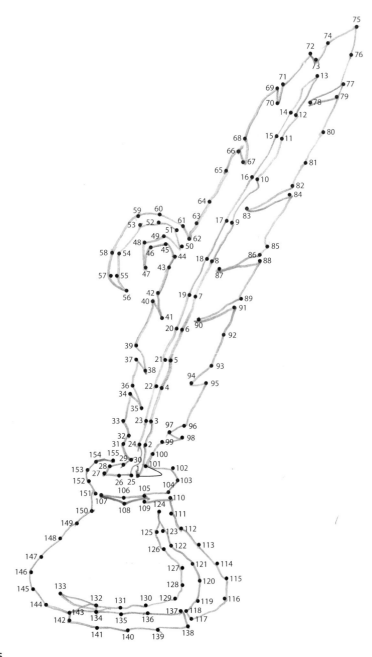

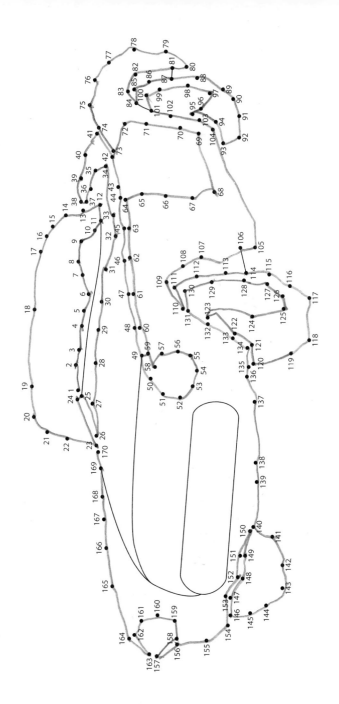

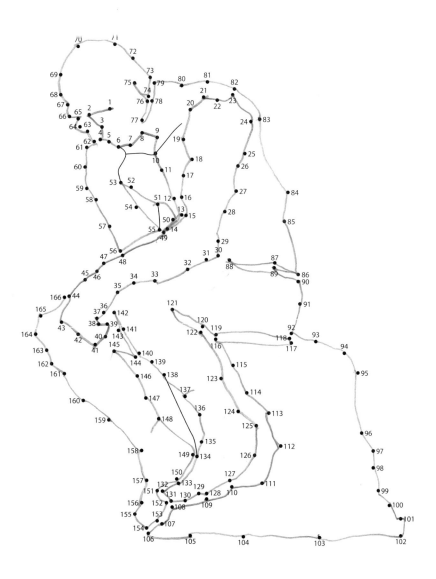

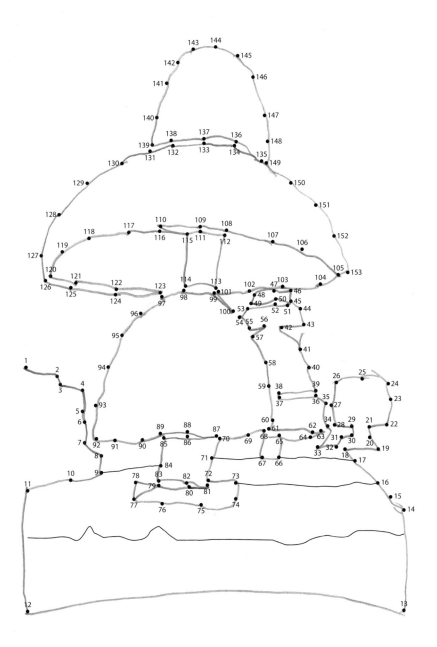

9

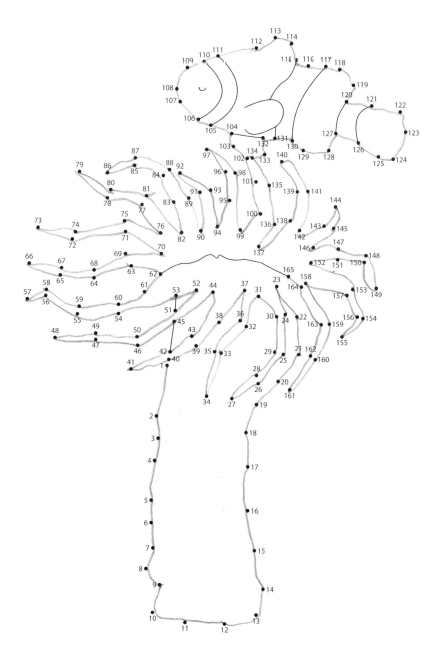

10

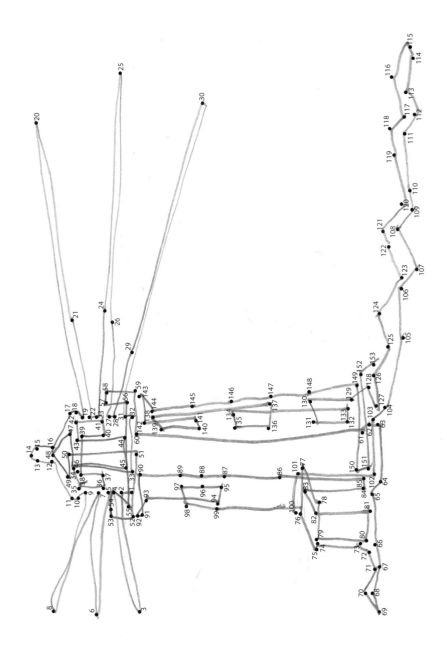

11

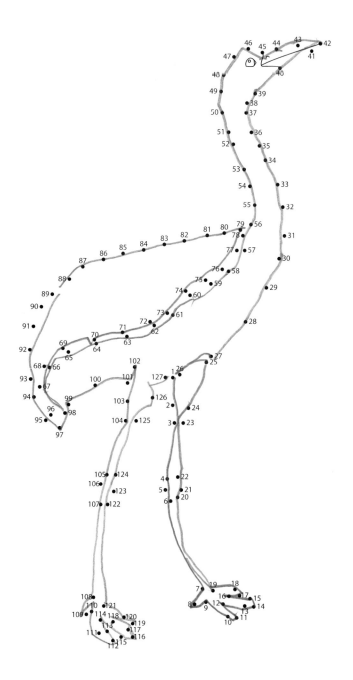

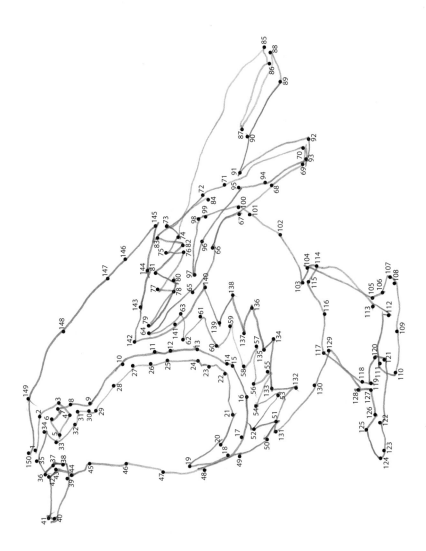

13

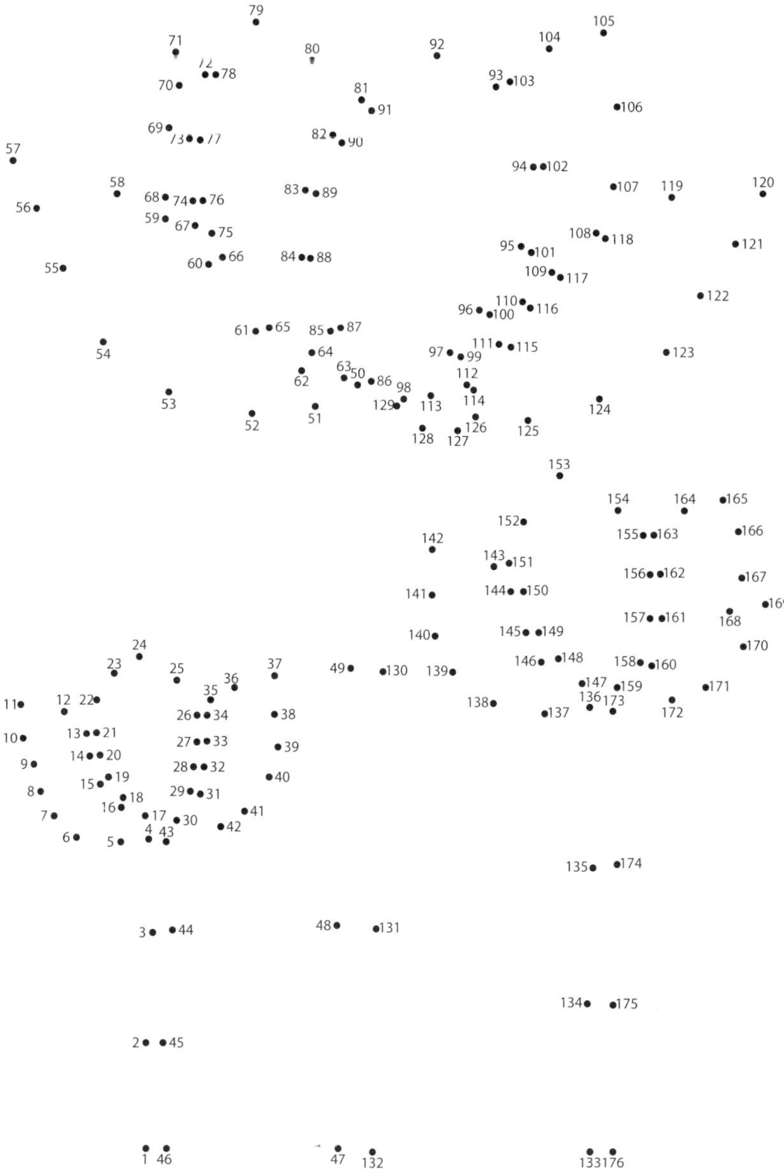

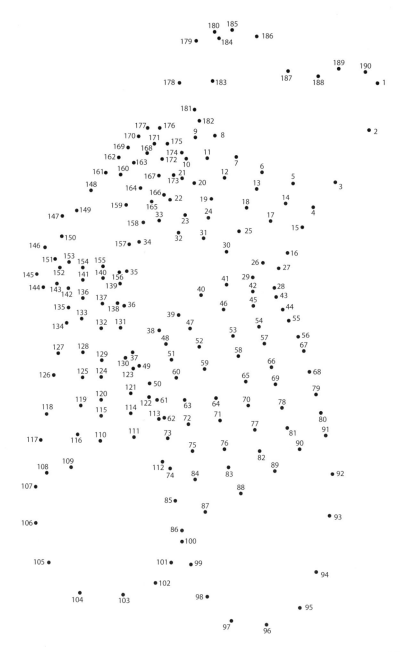

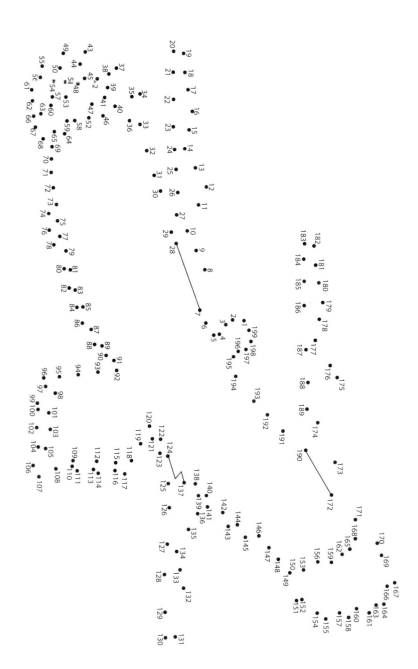

16

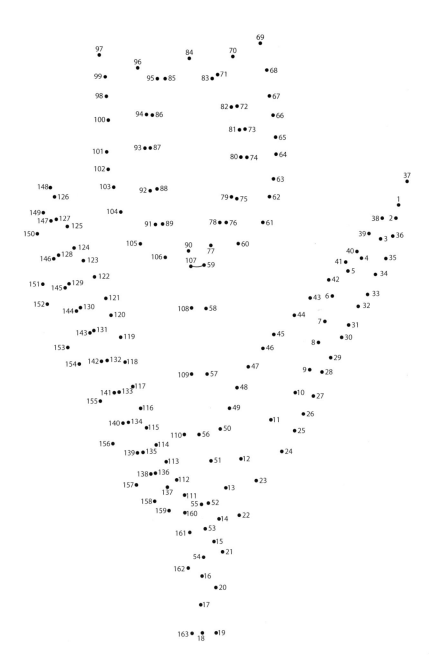

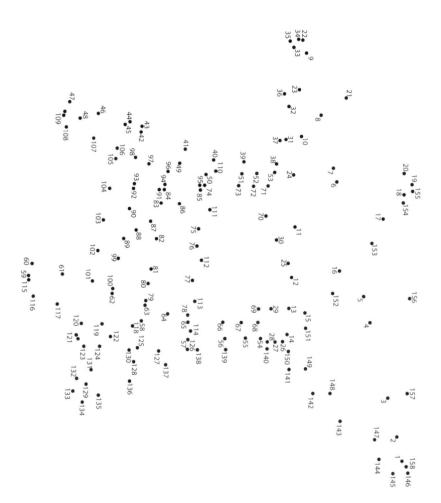

19

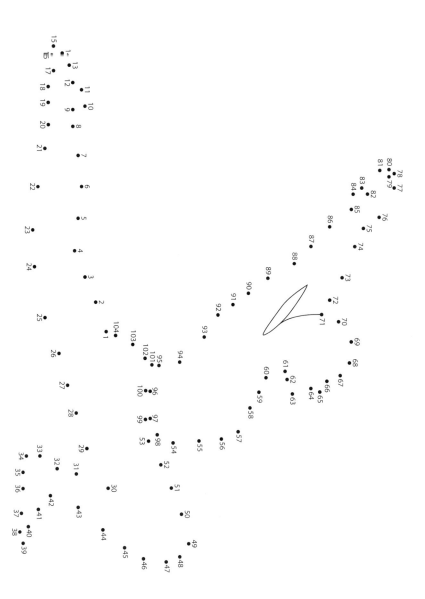

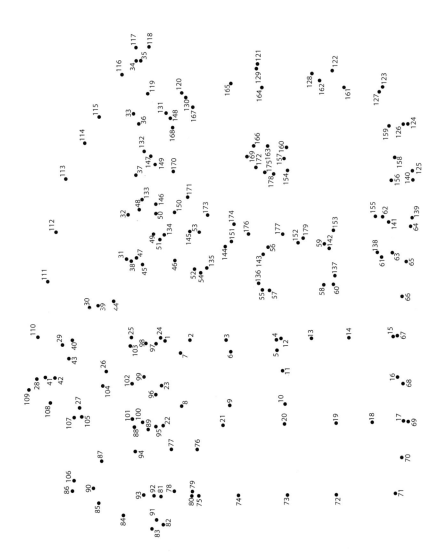

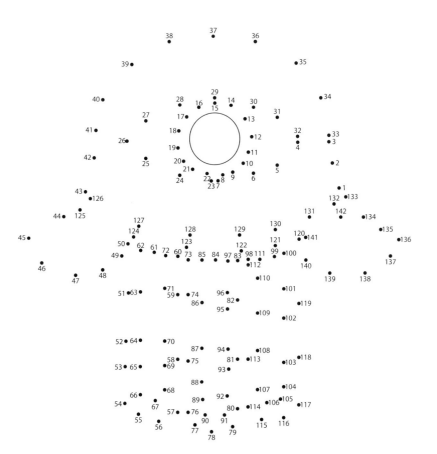

23

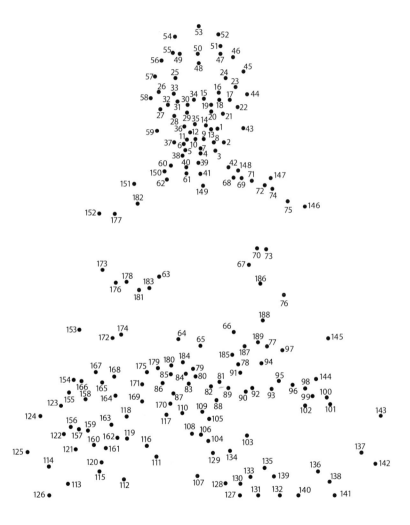

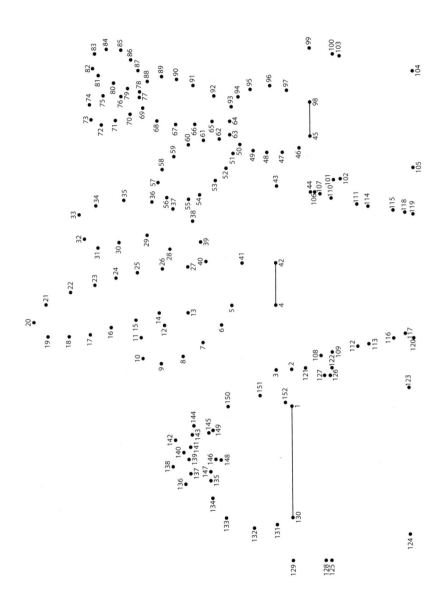

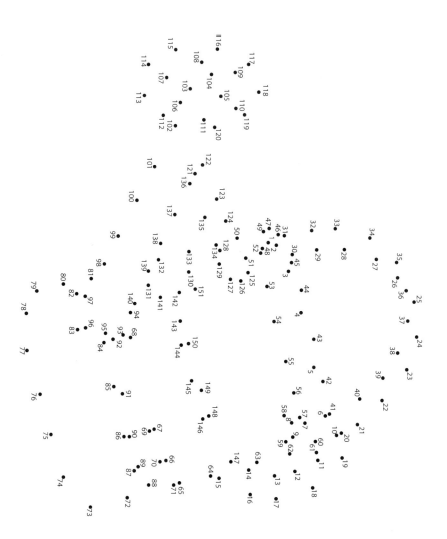

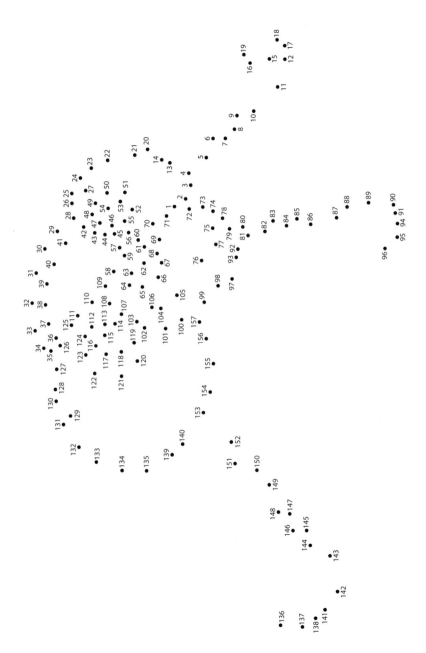

27

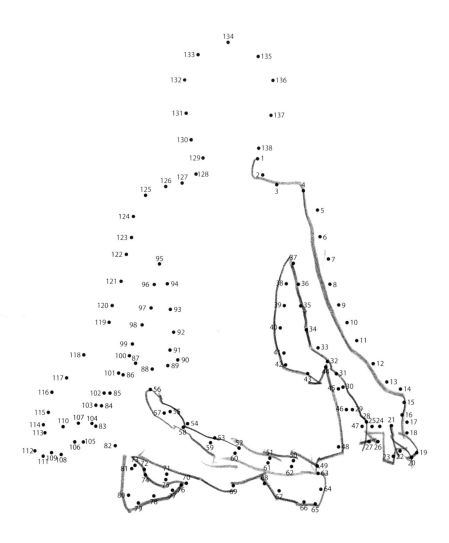

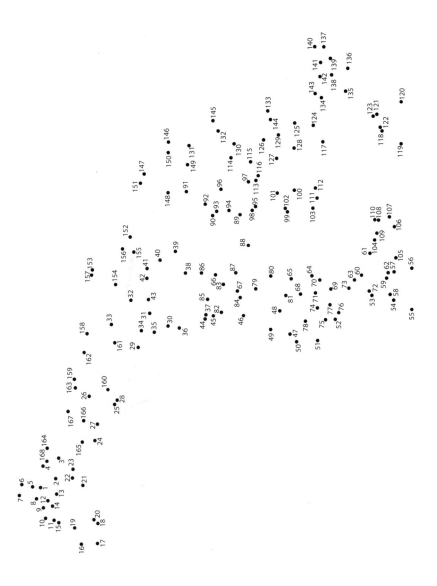

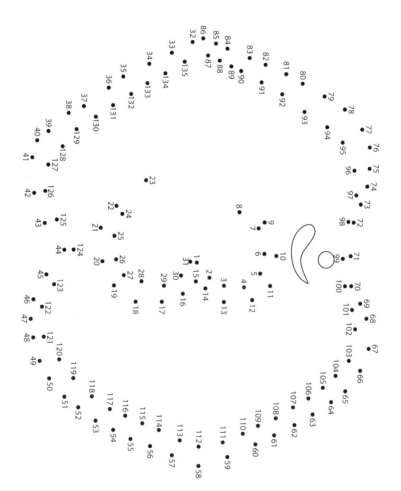

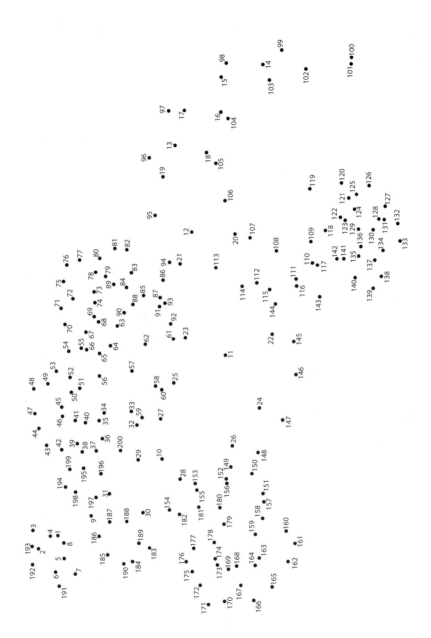

31

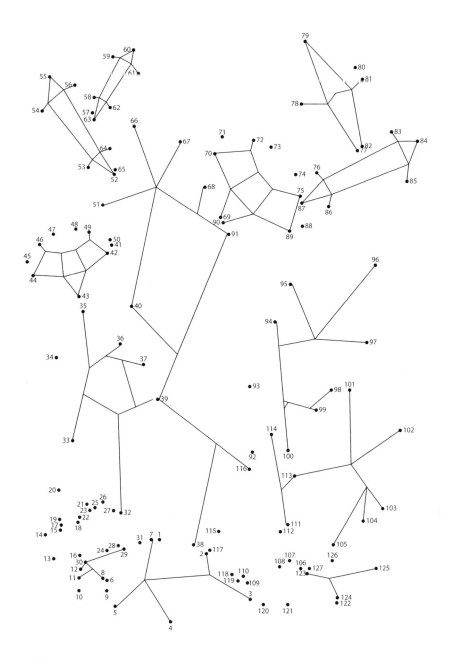

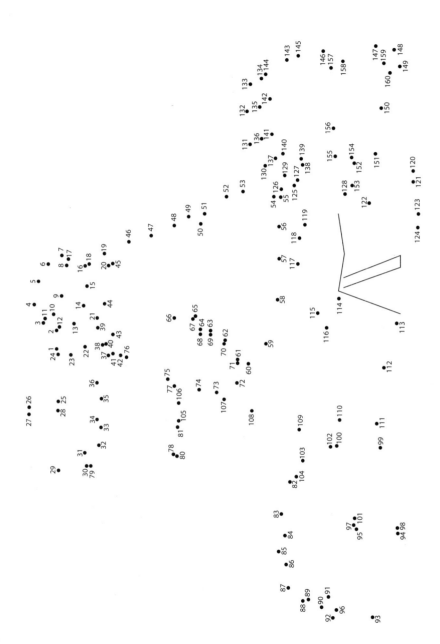

33

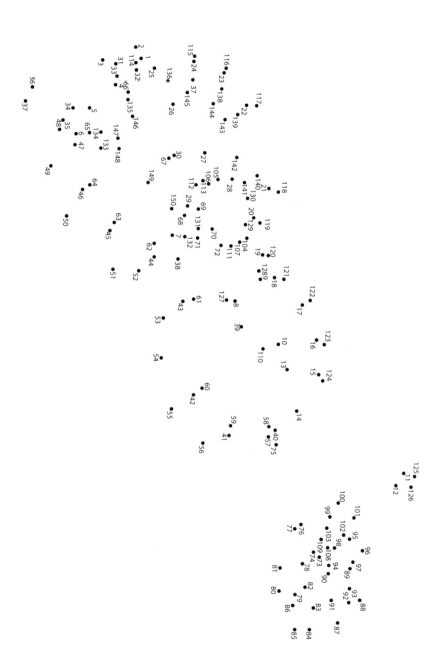

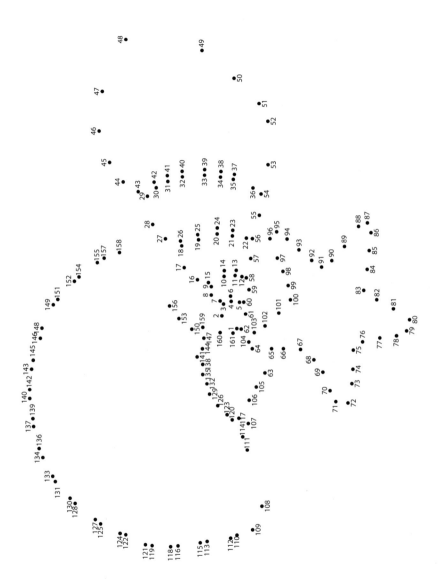

35

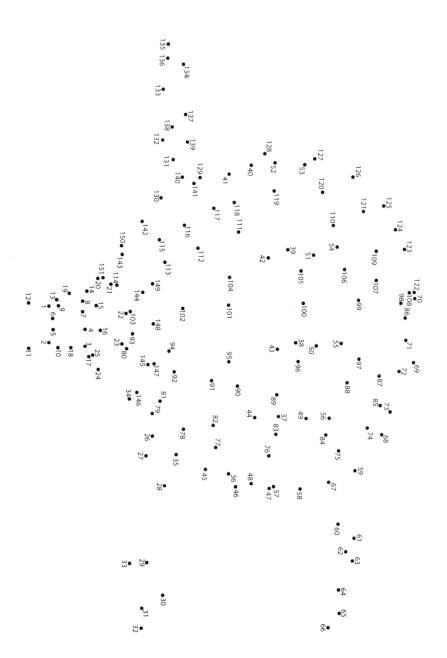

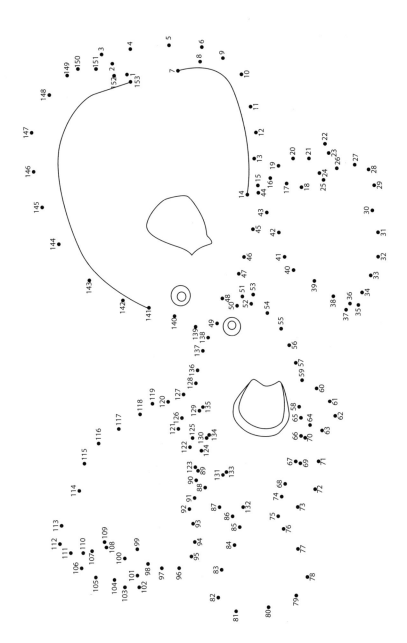

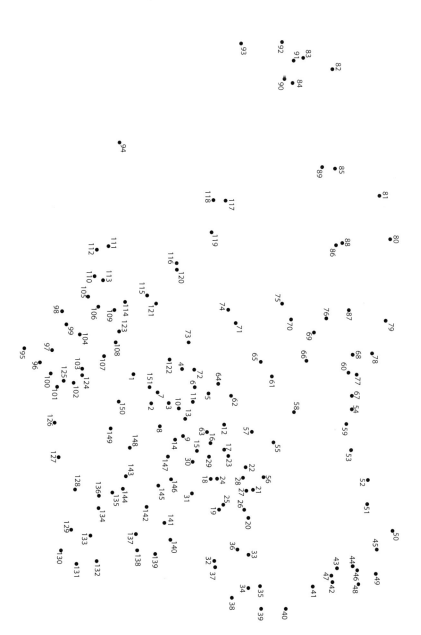

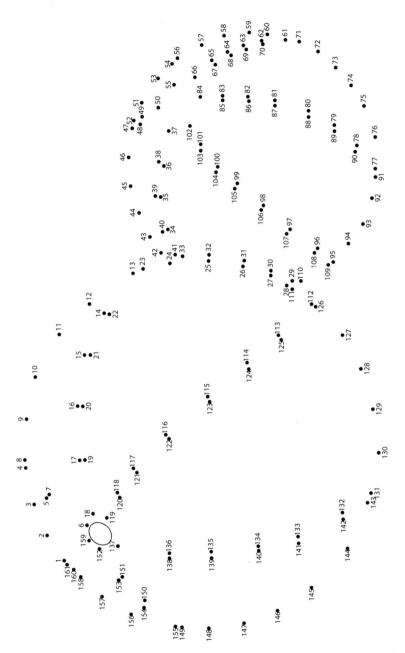

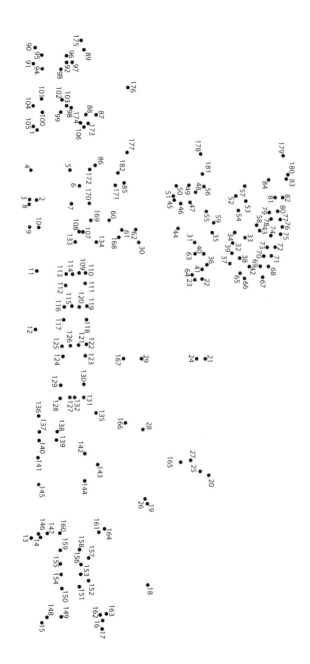

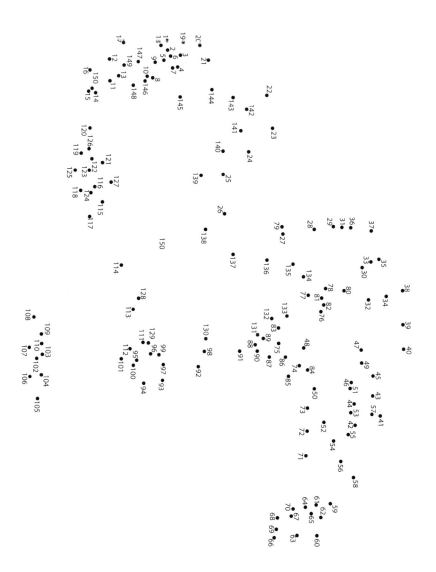

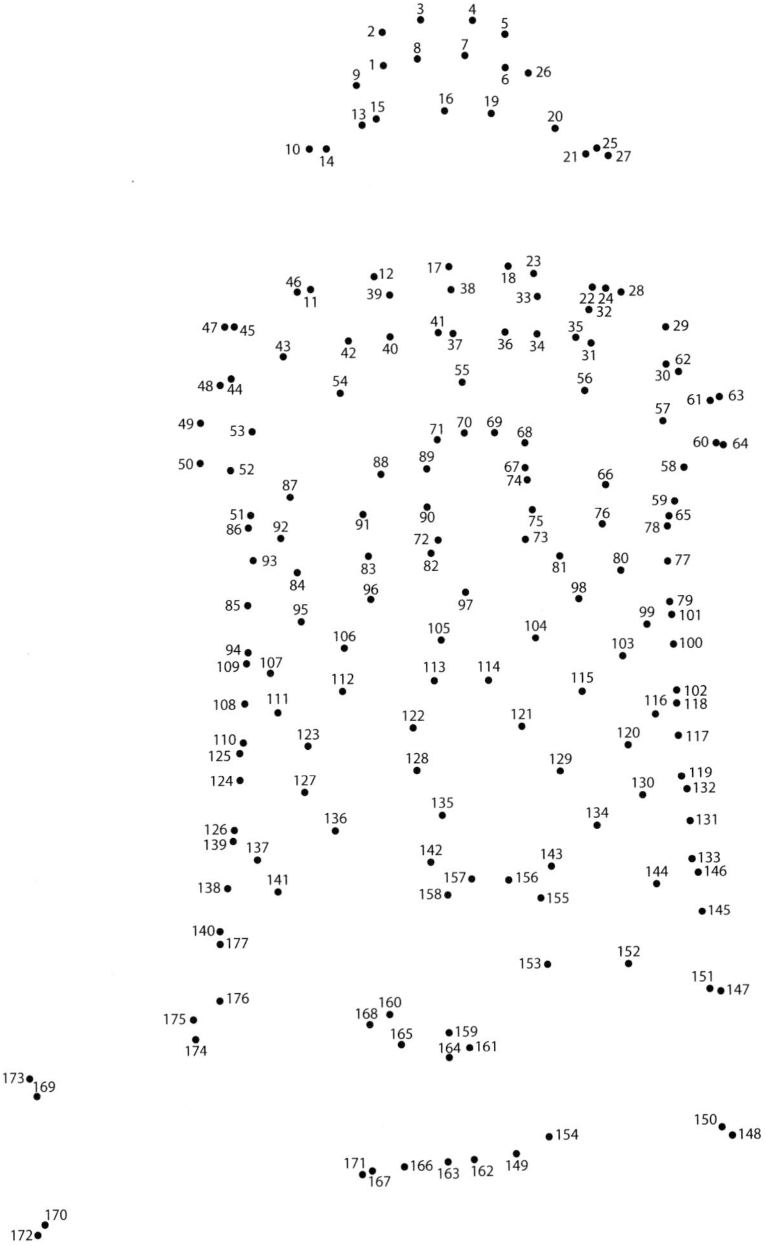

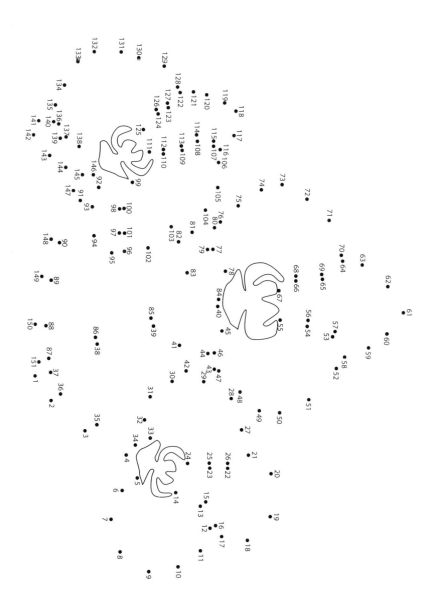

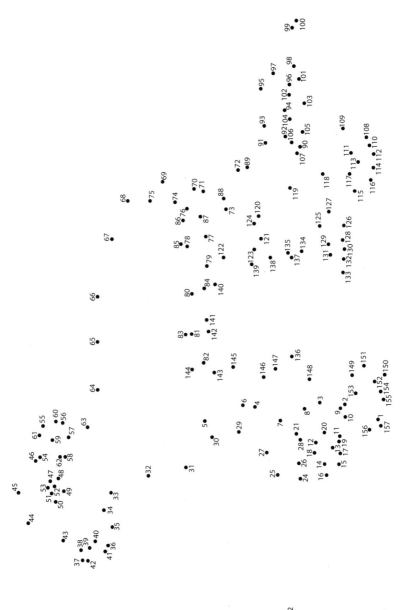

45

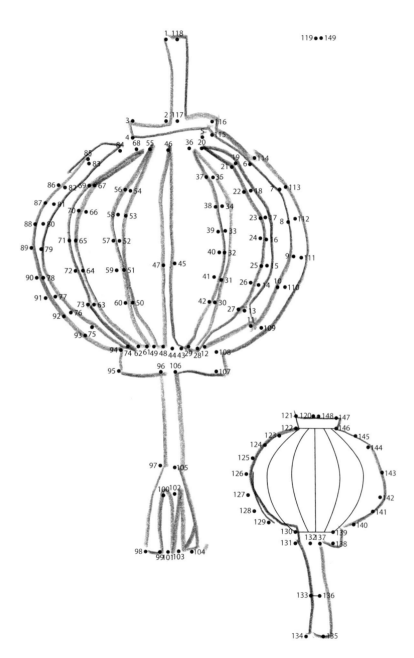

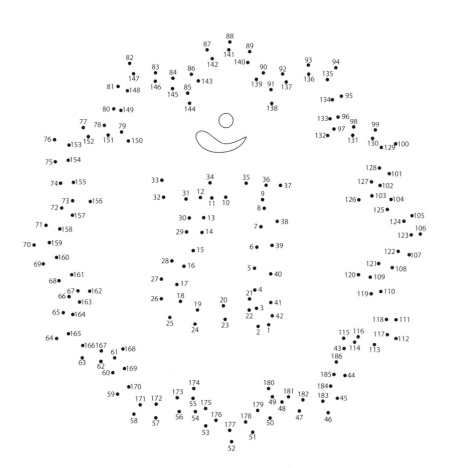

48

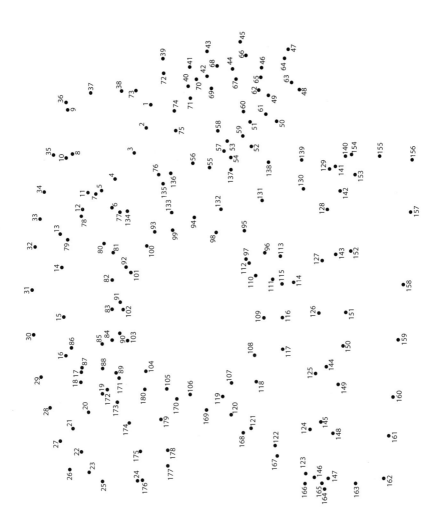

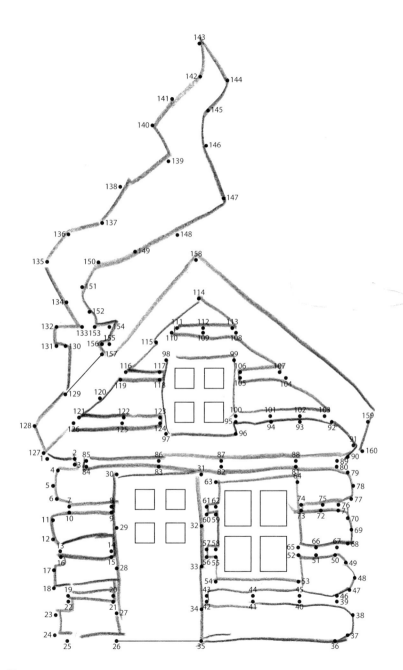

50

51

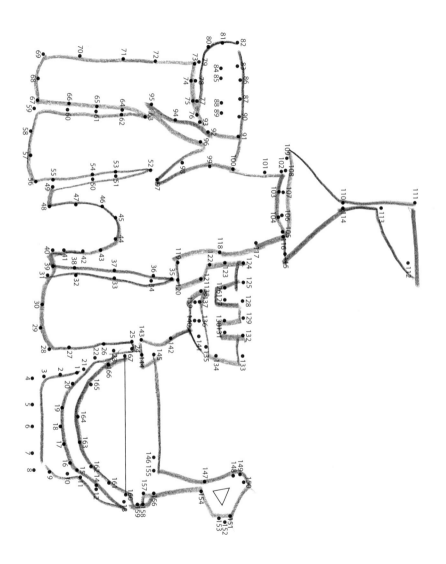

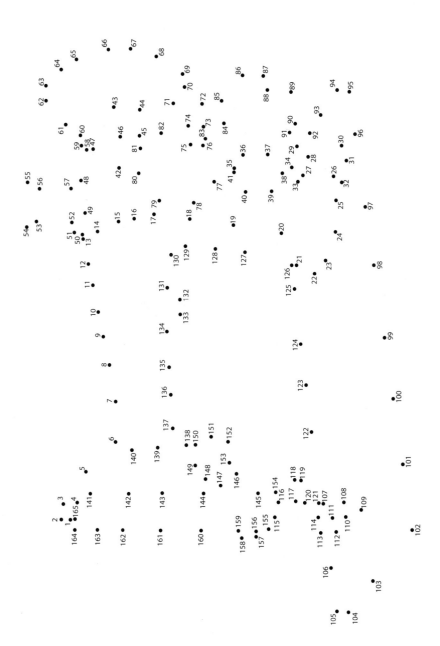

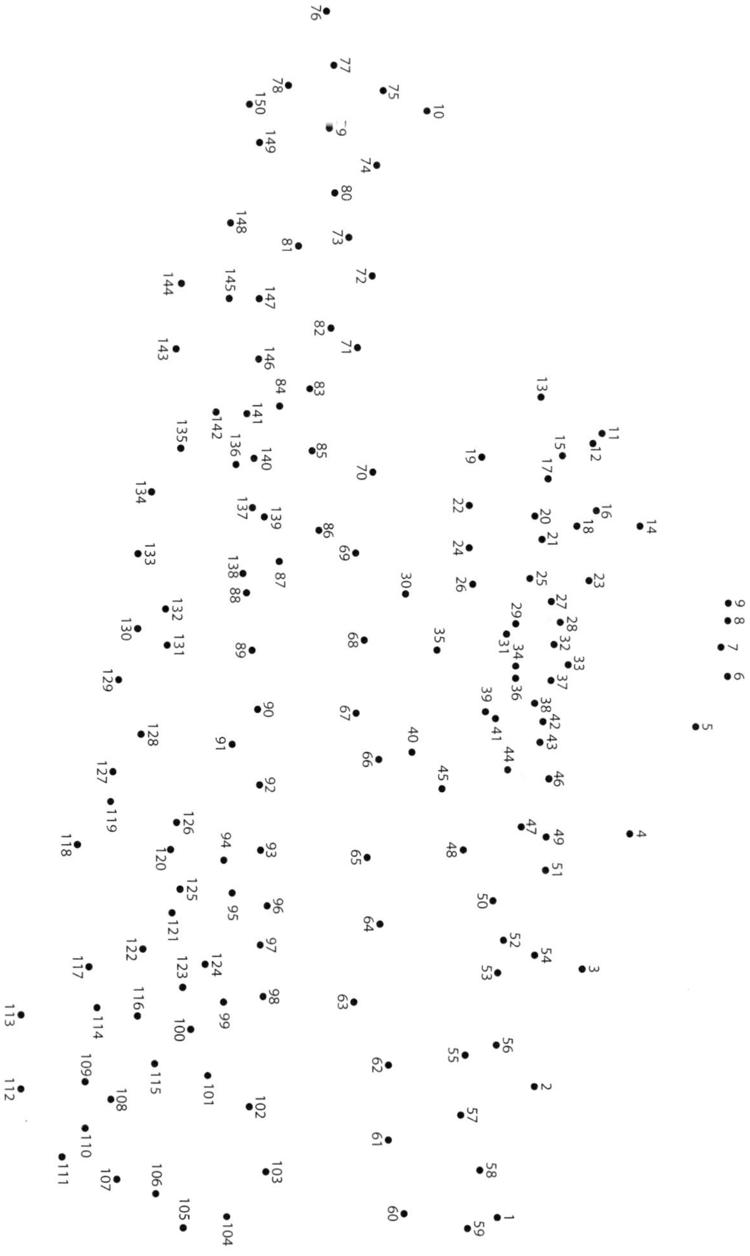

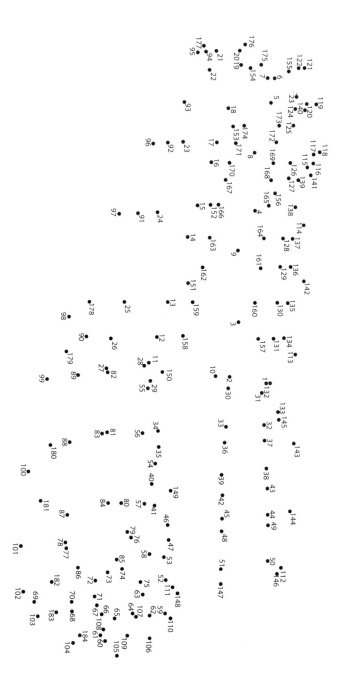

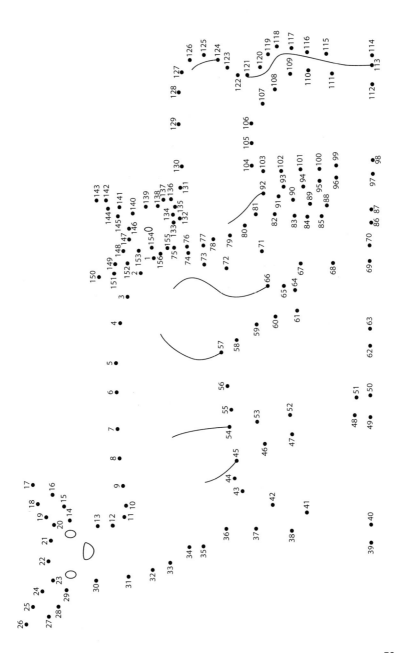

60

61

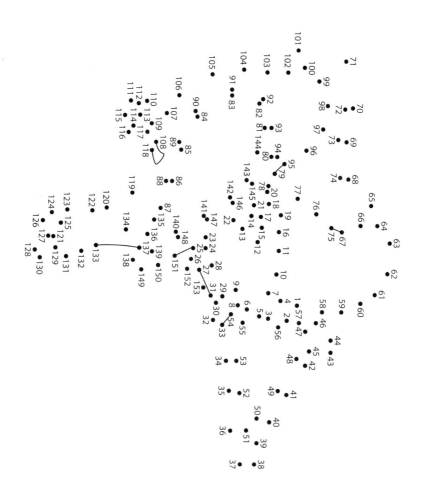

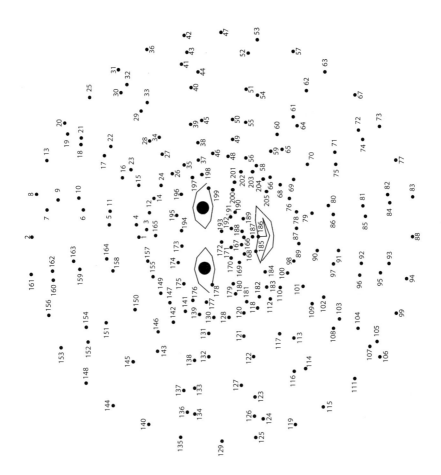

63

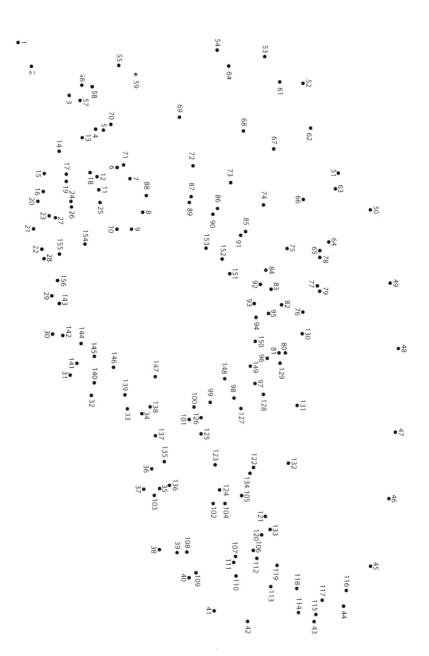

64

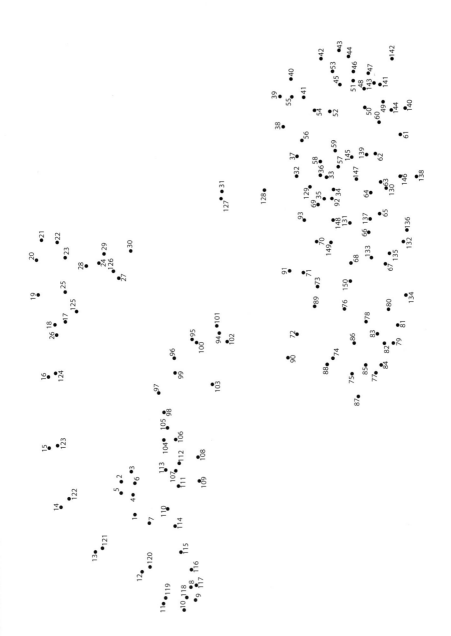

65

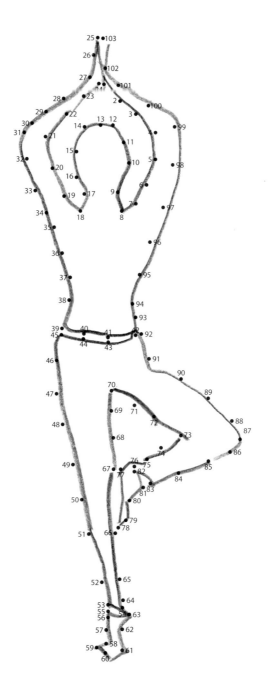

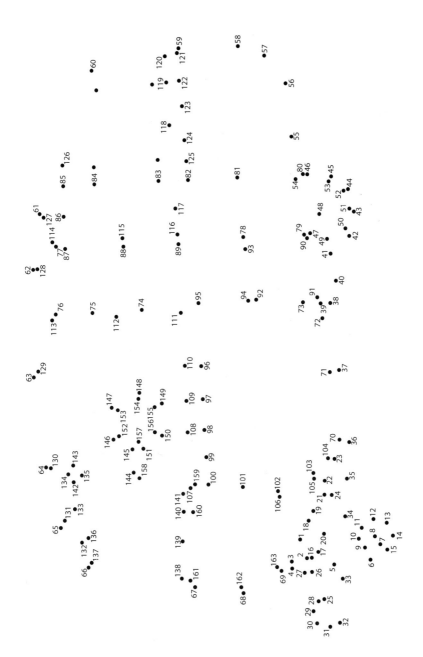

67

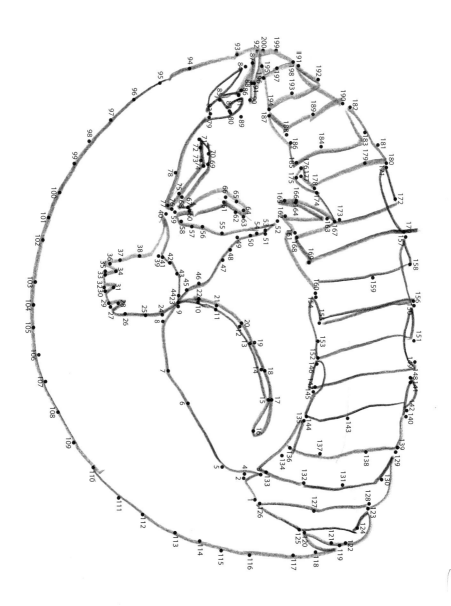

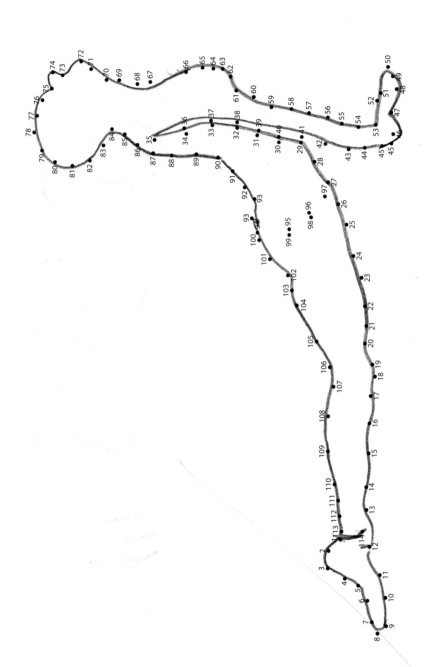

71

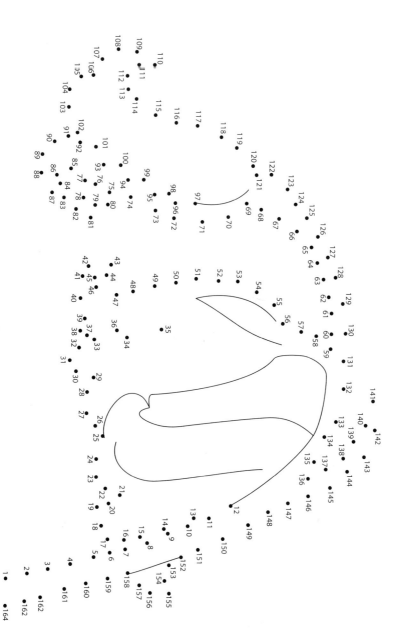

72

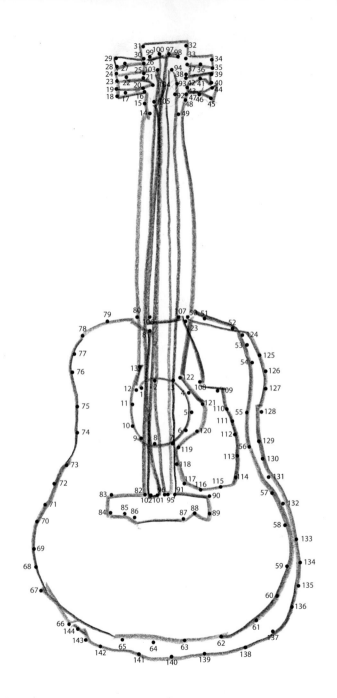

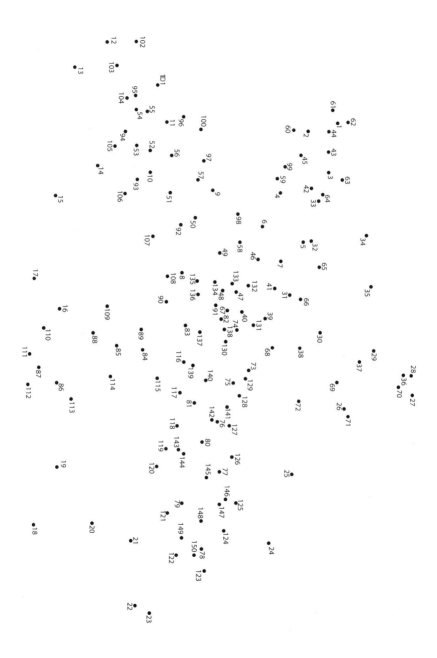

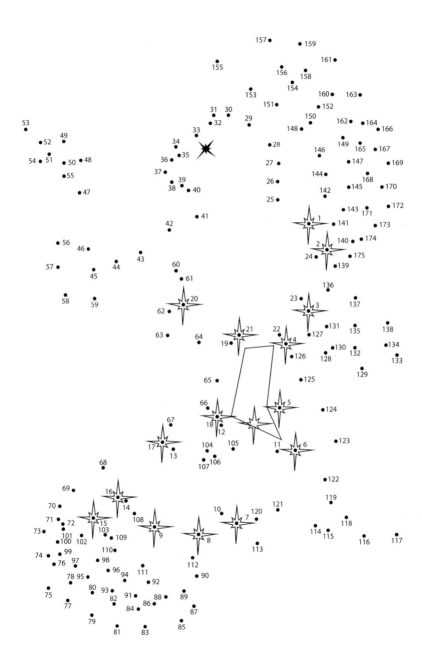

75

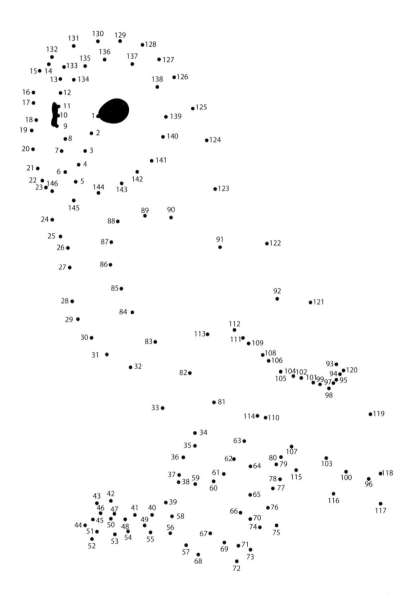

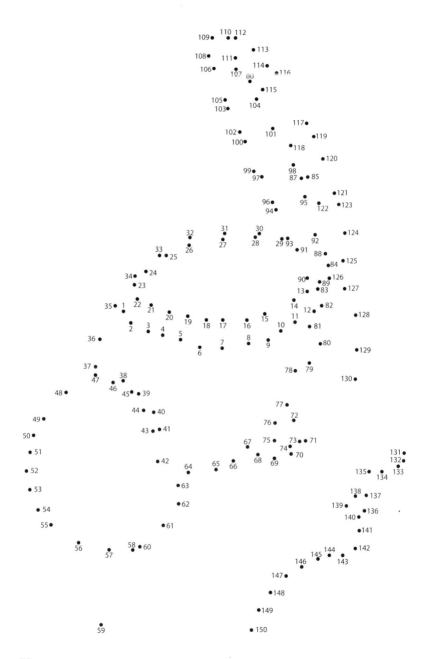

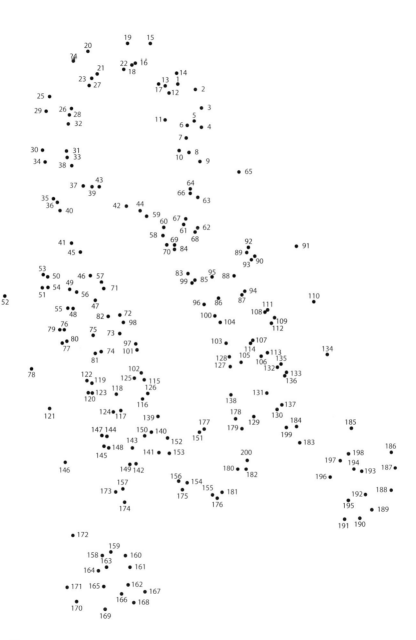

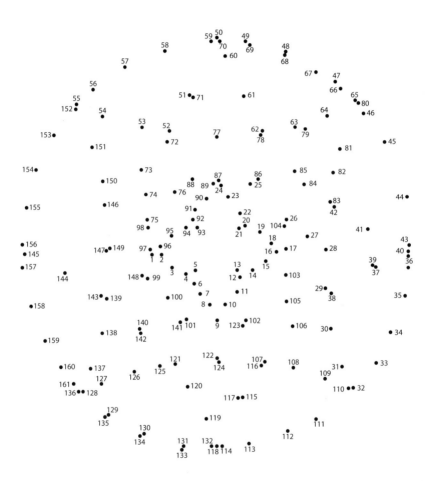

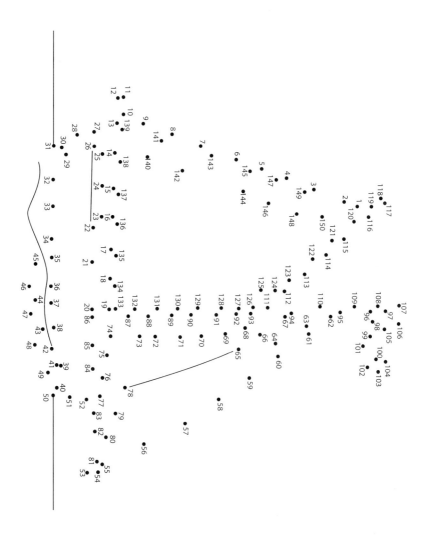

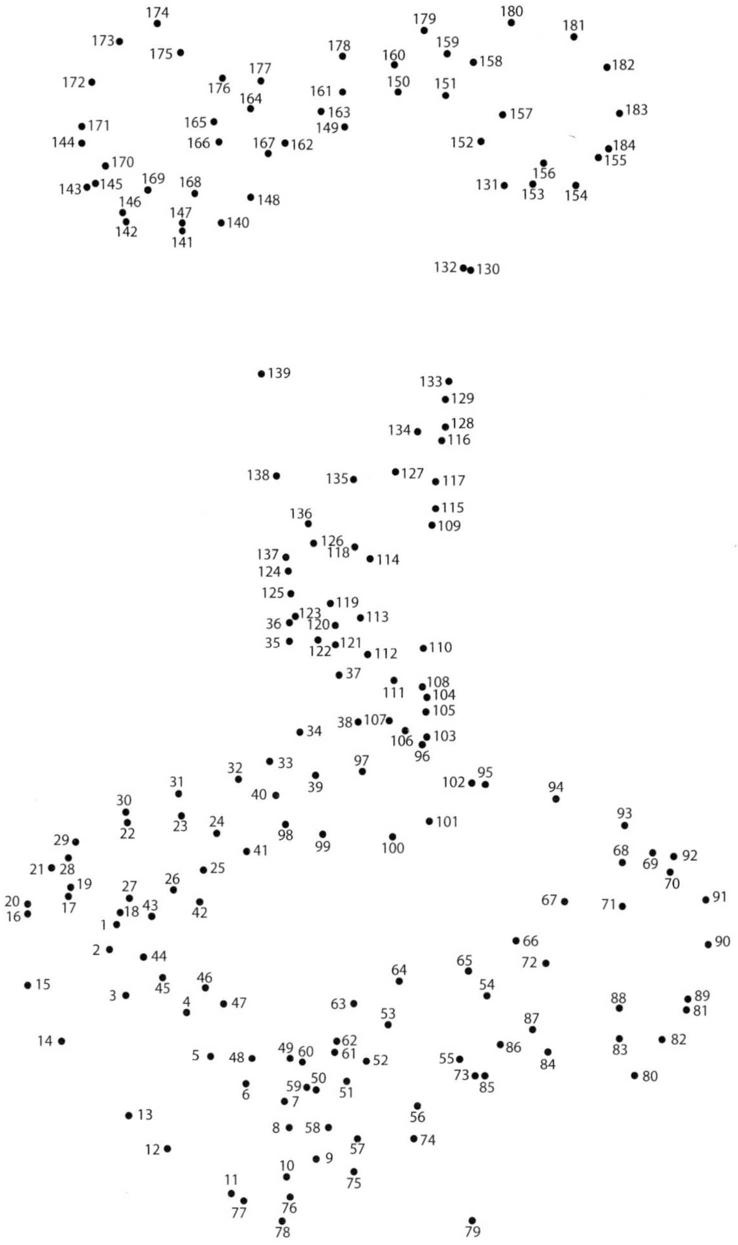

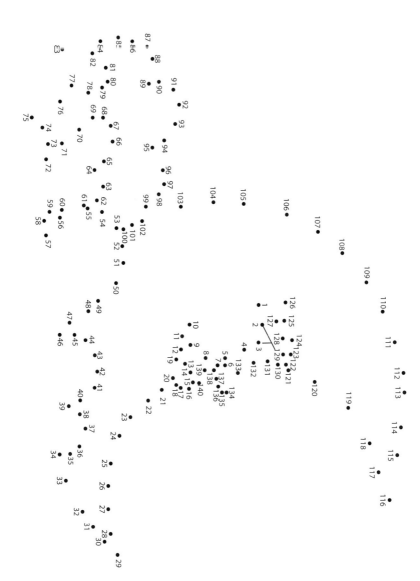

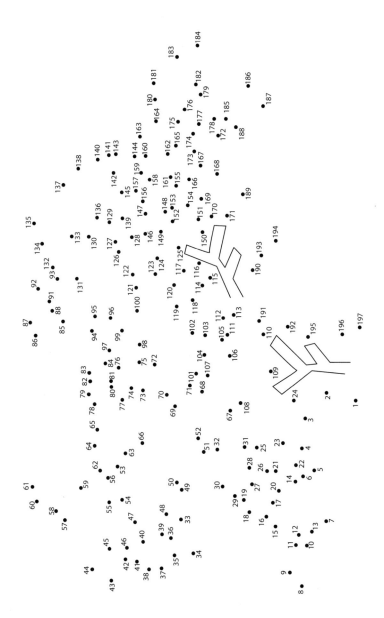

85

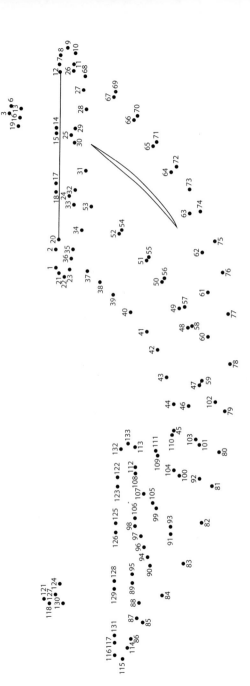

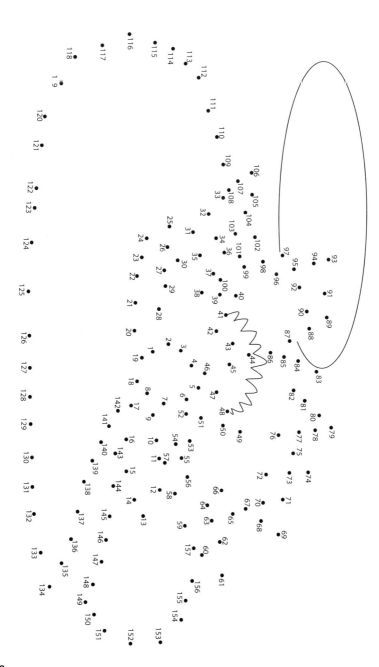

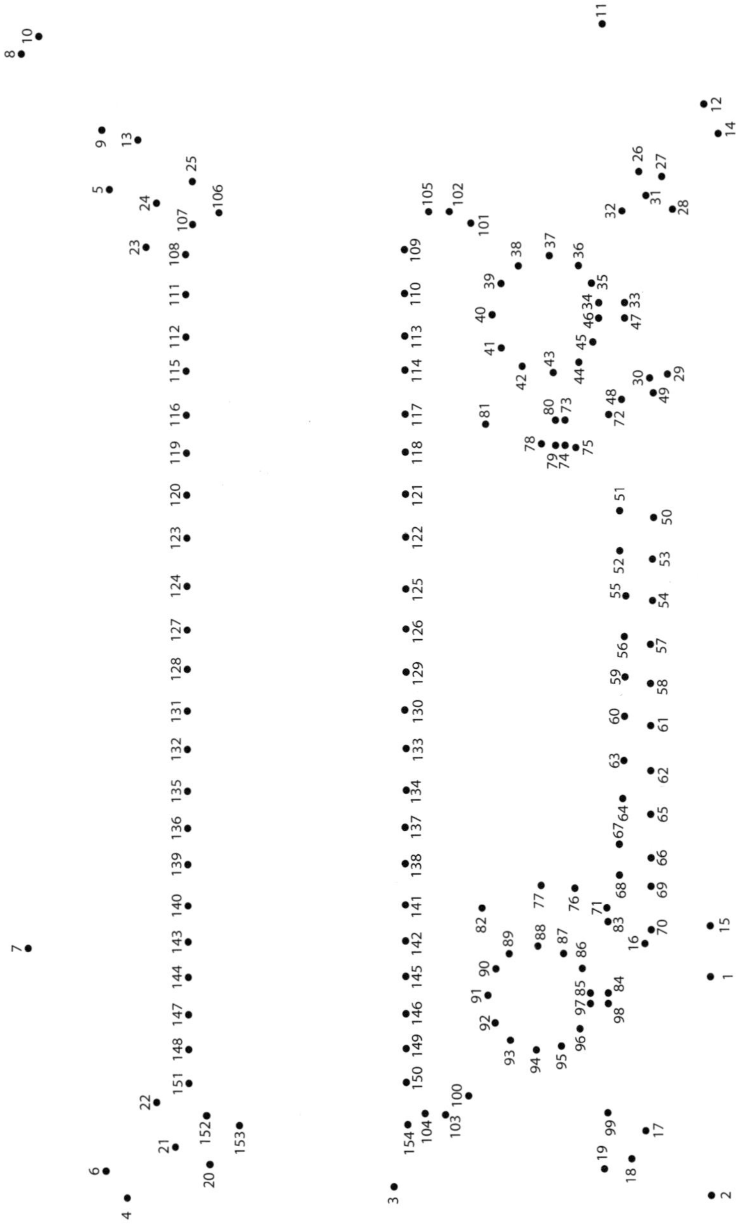

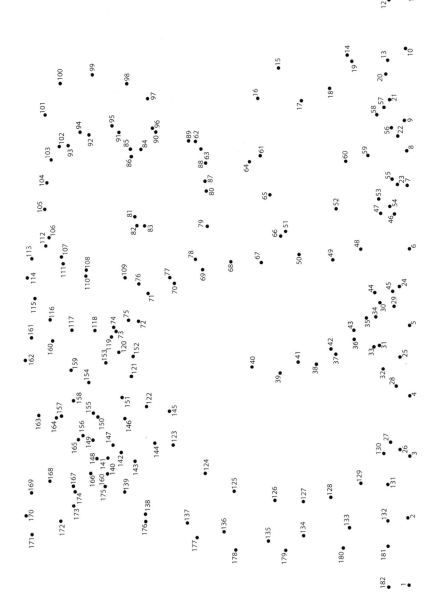

91

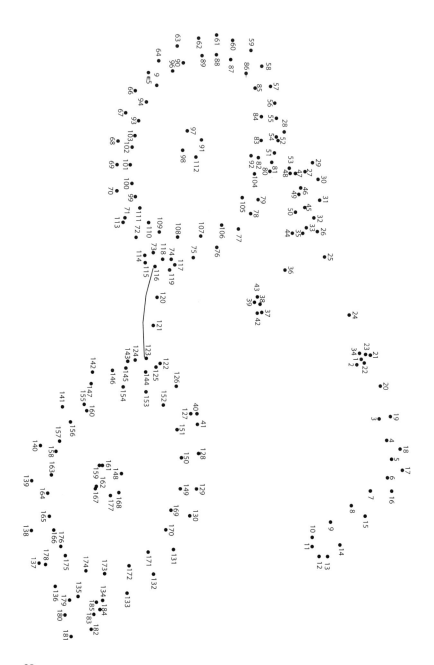

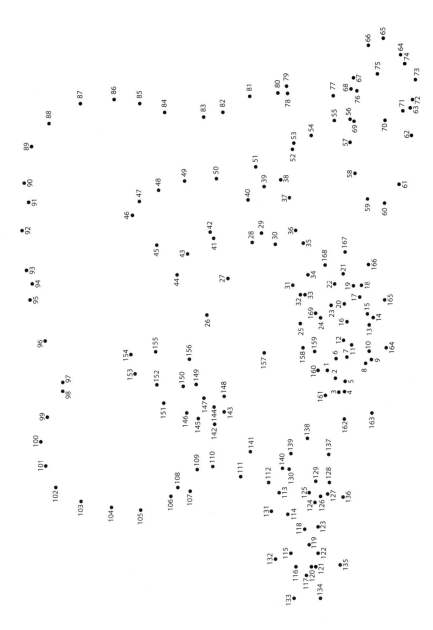

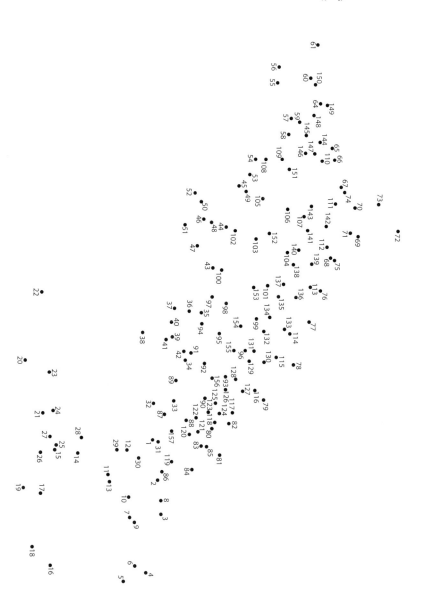

94

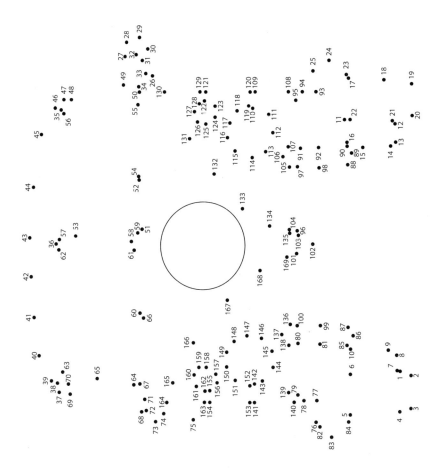

95

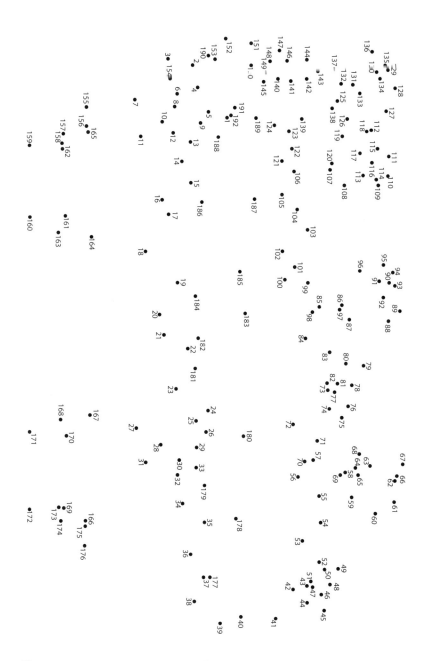

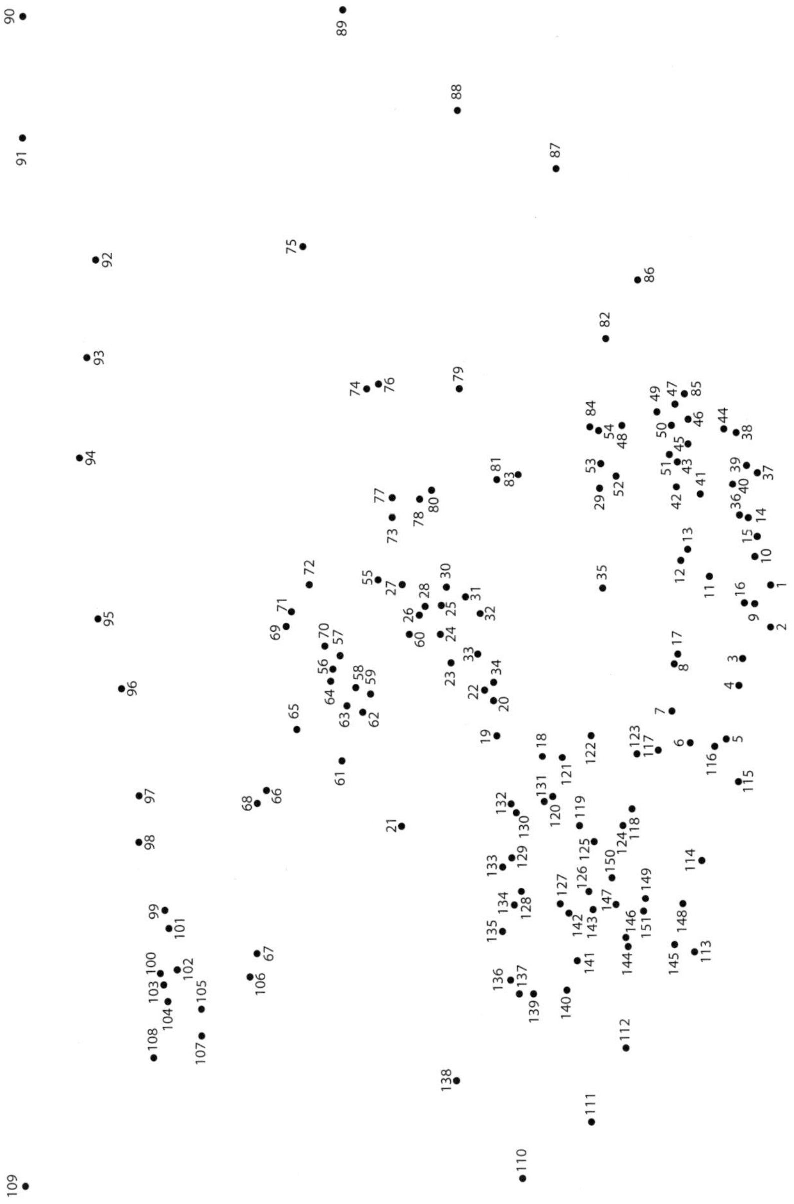

100

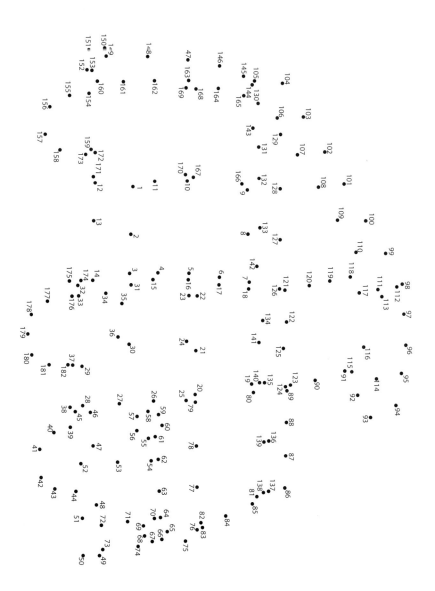

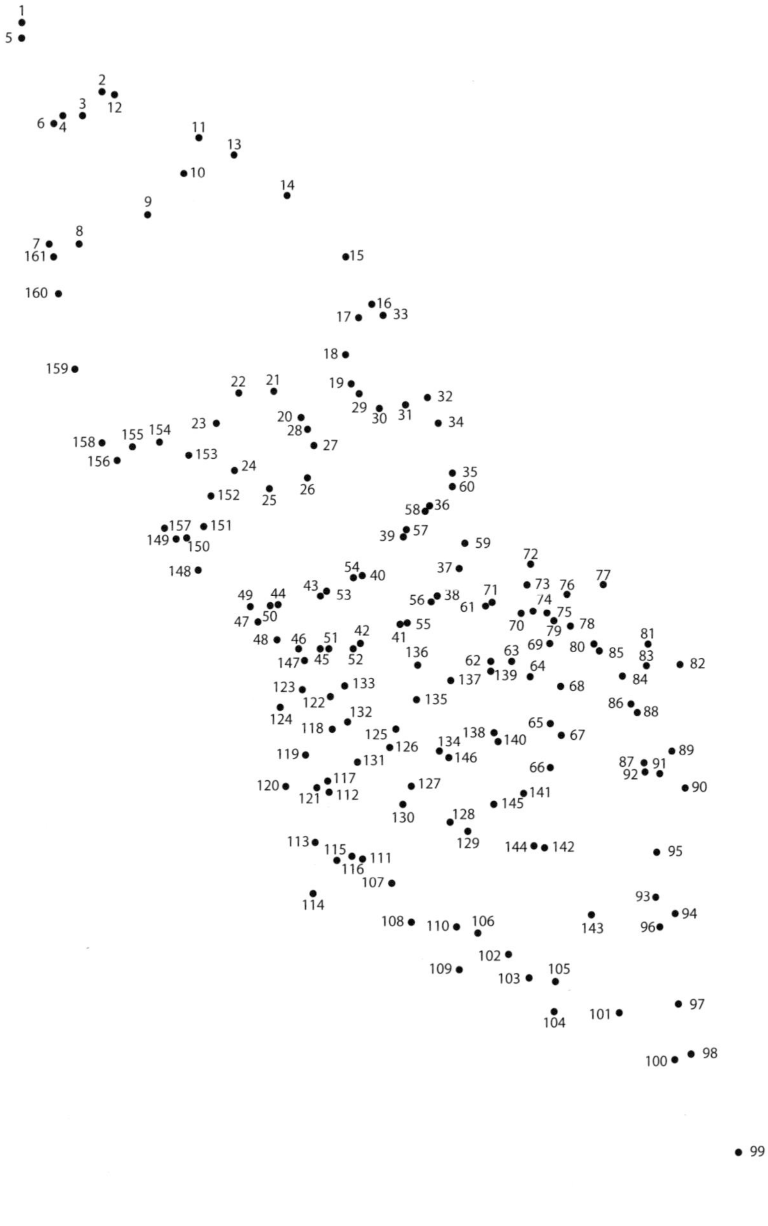

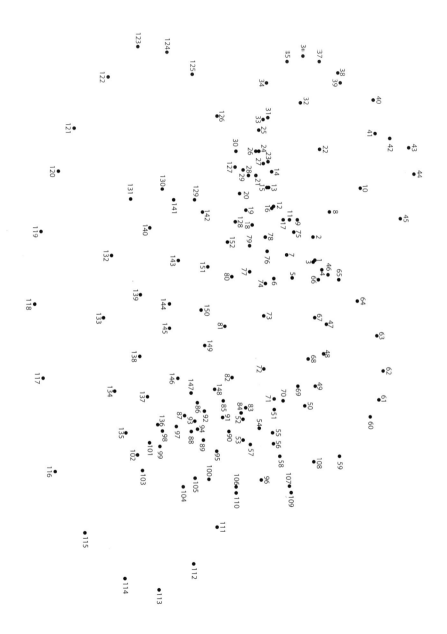

104

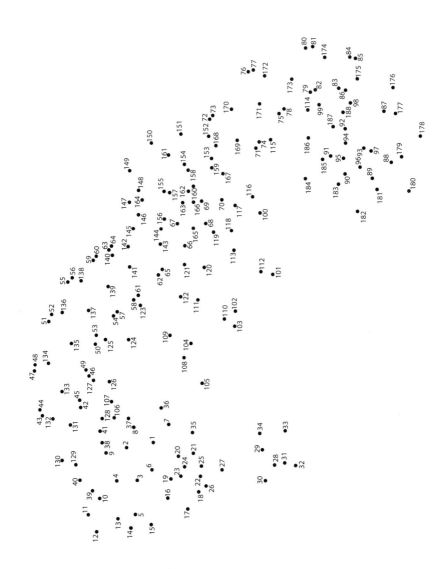

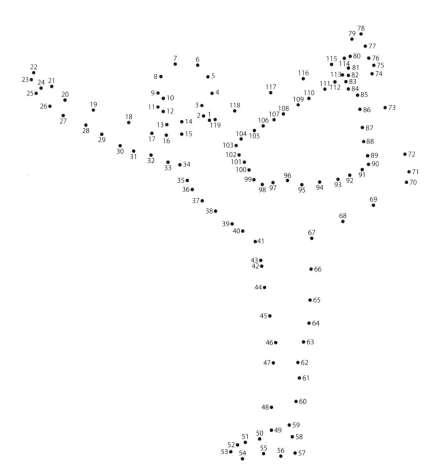

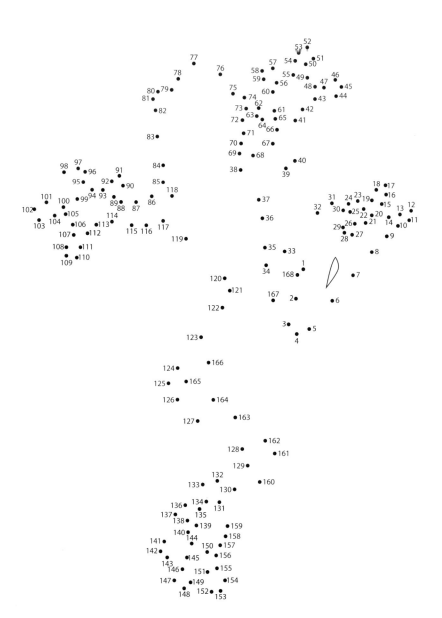

109

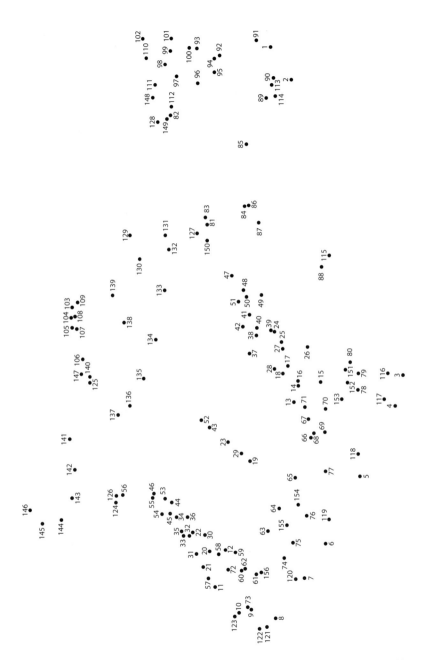

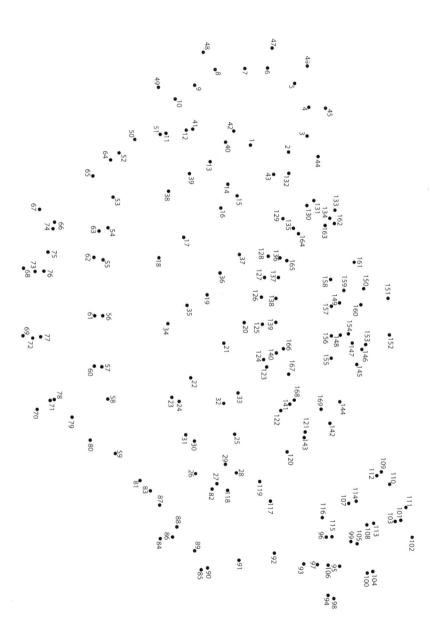

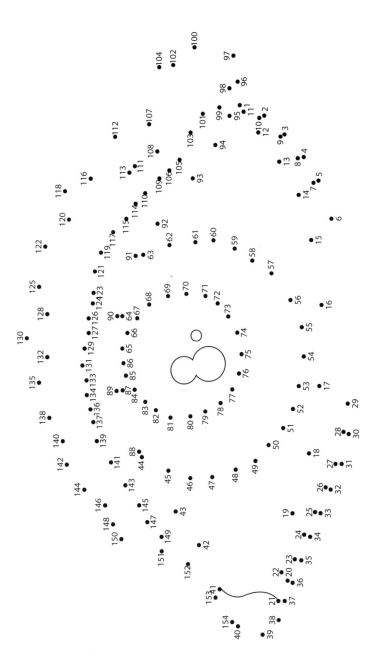

113

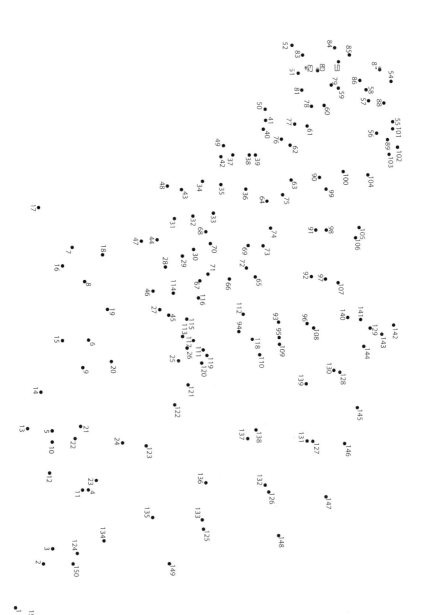

114

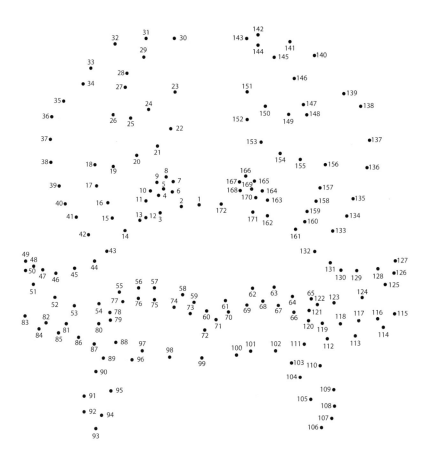

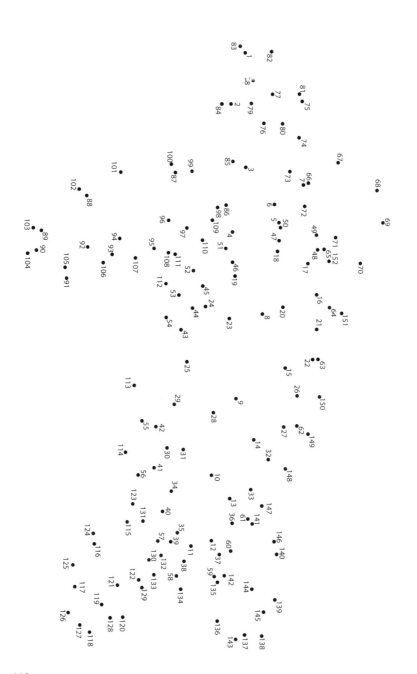

116

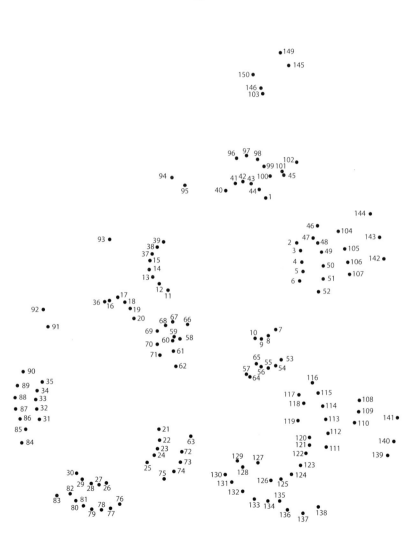

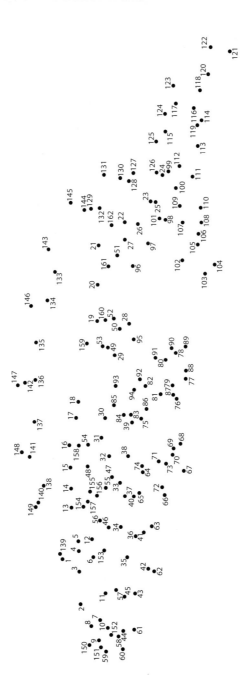

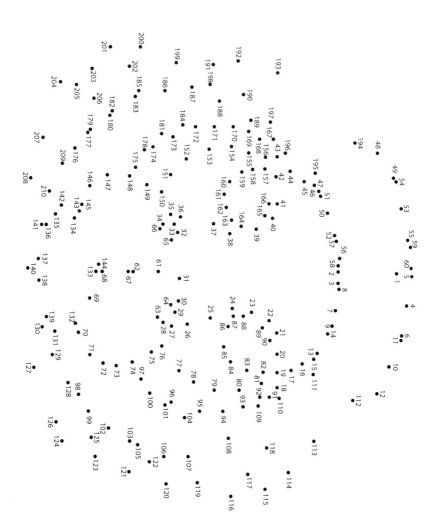

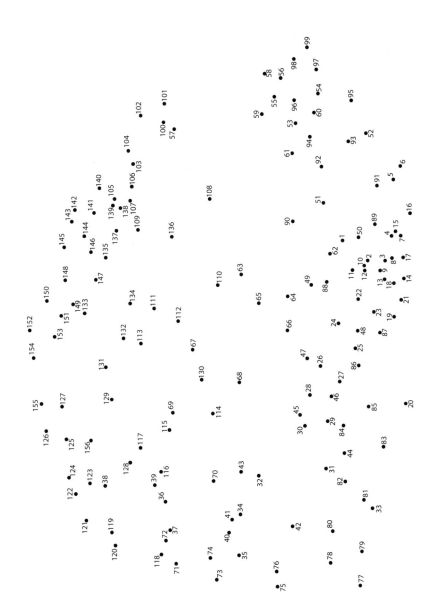

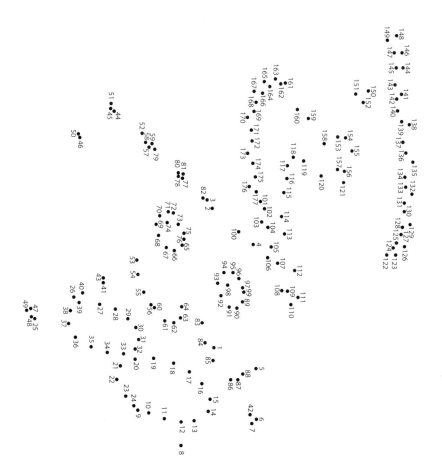

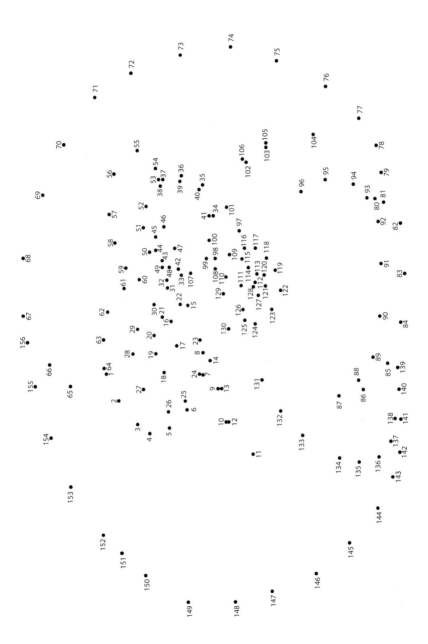

123

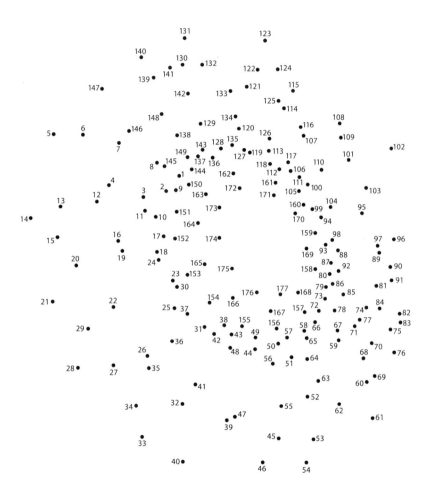

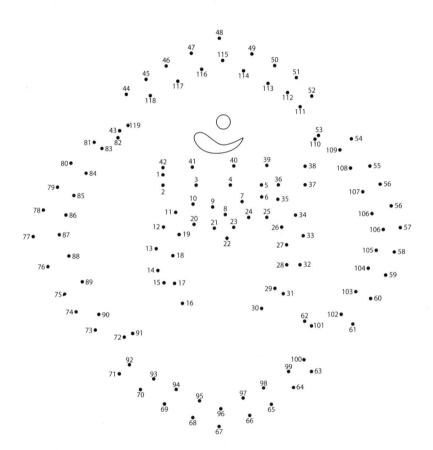

126

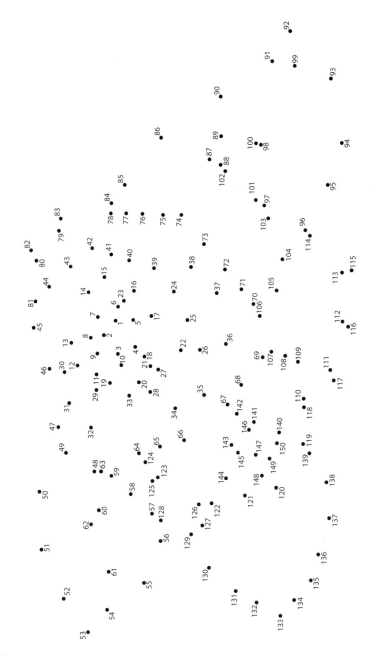

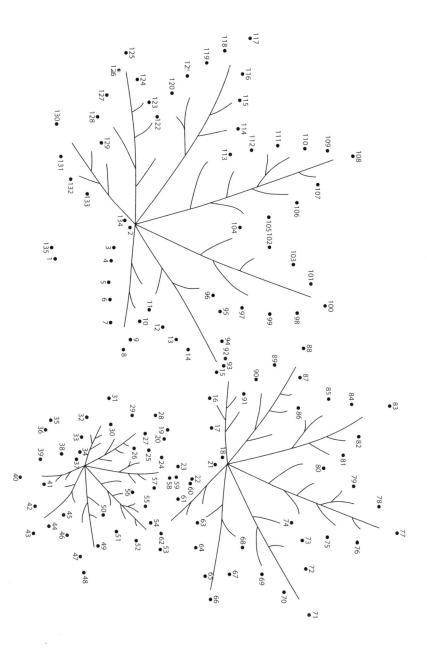

128

129

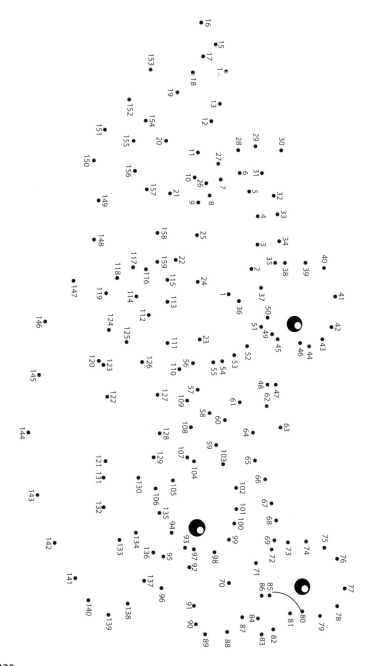

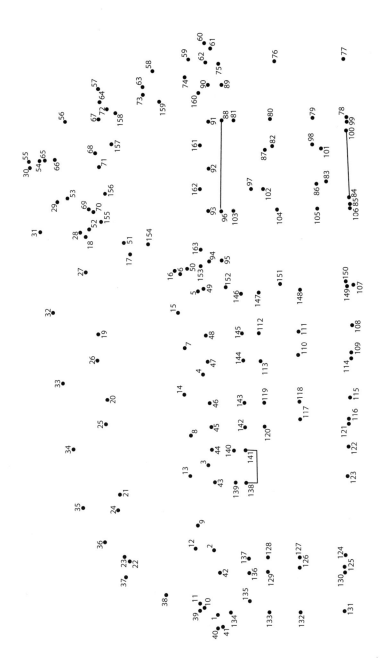

131

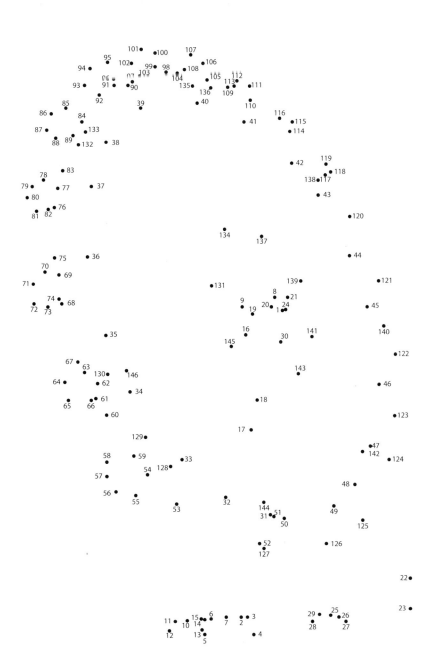

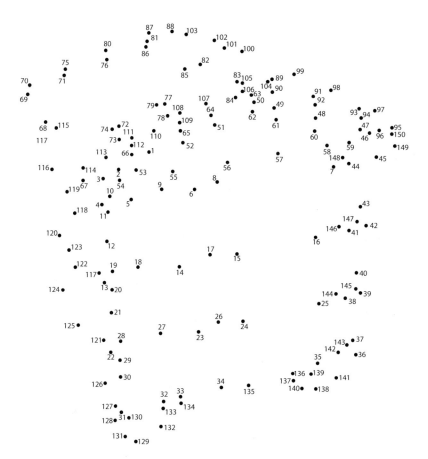

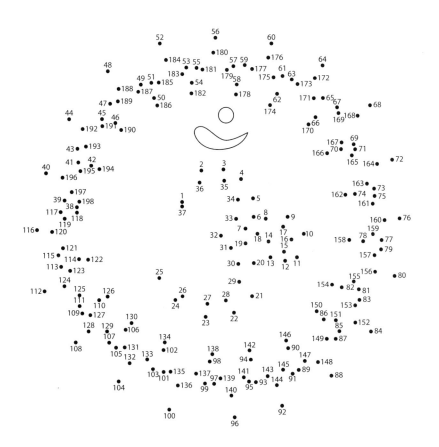

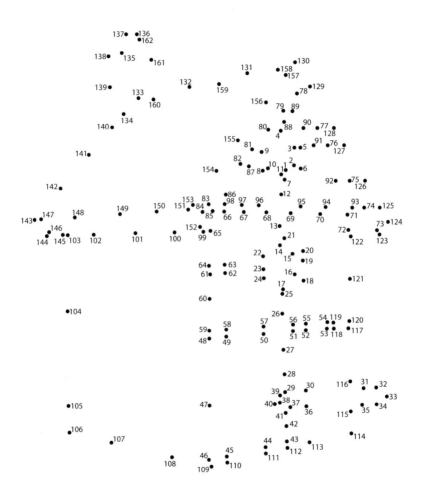

136

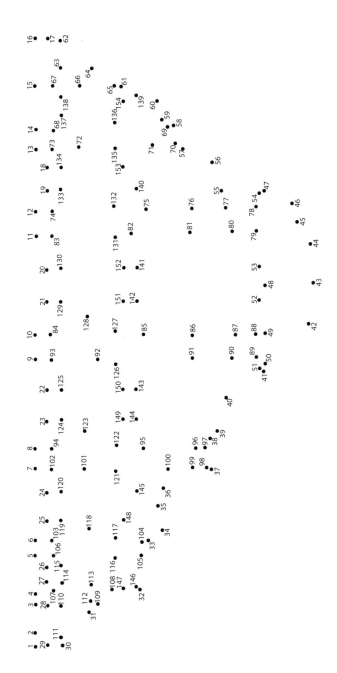

137

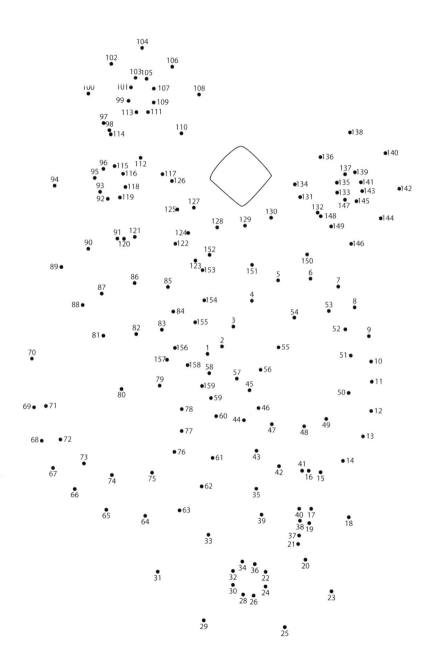

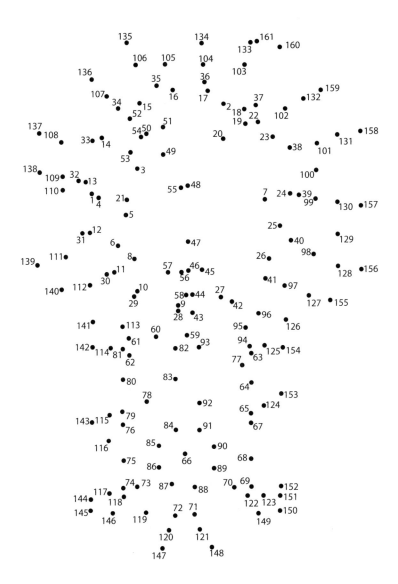

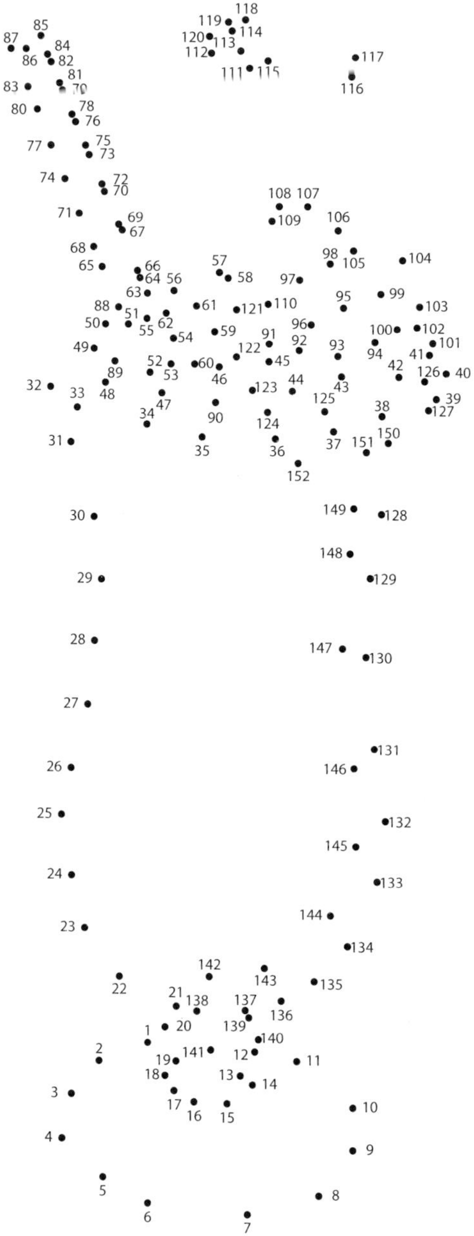

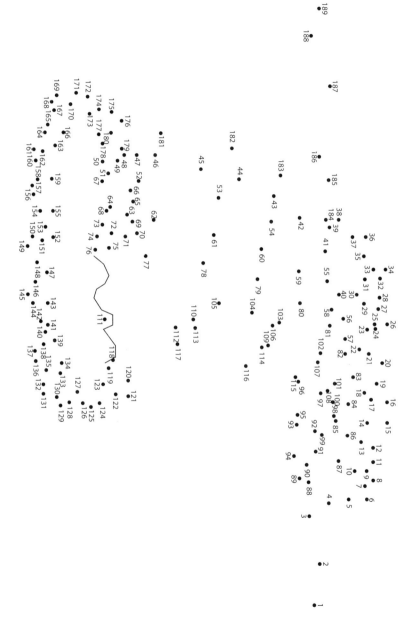

143

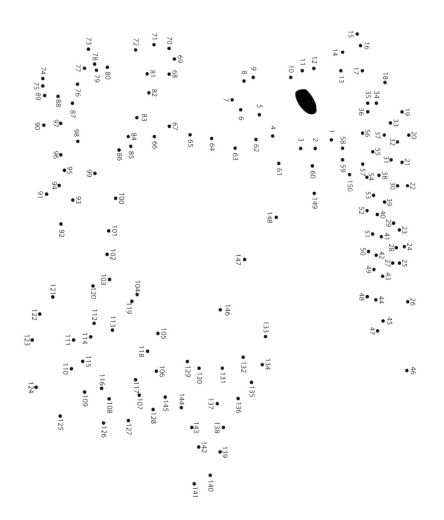

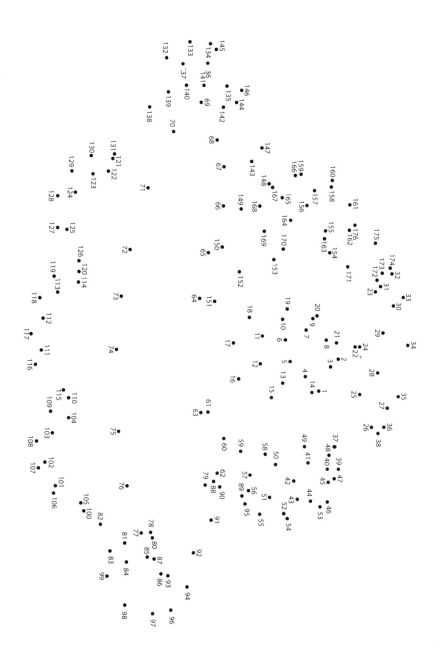

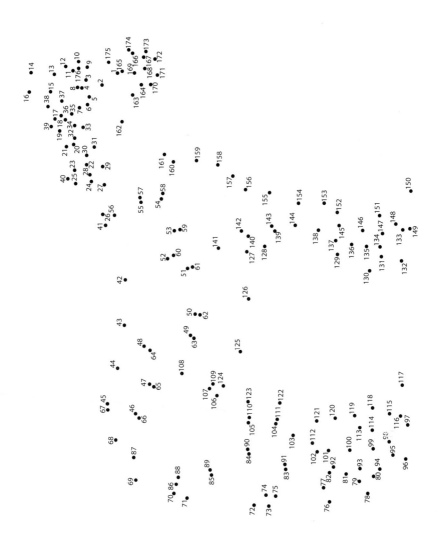

147

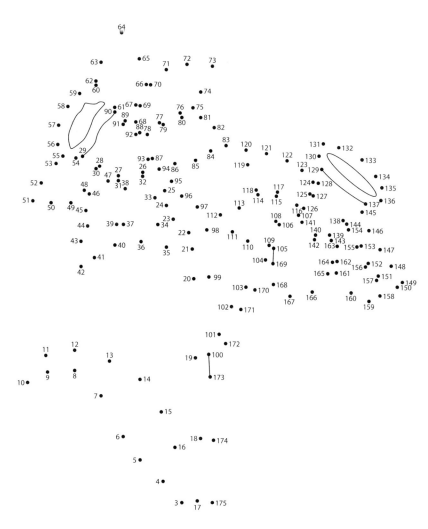

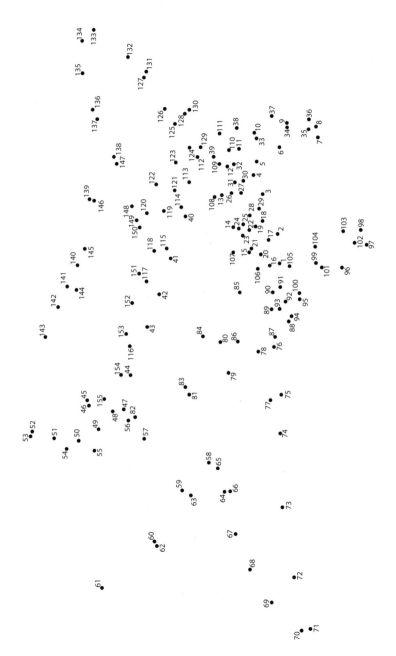

149

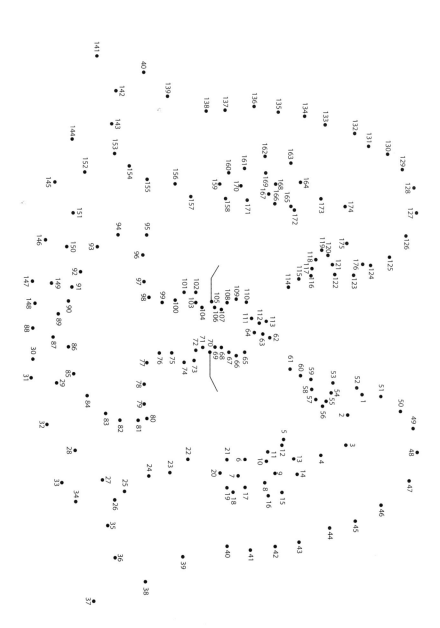

150

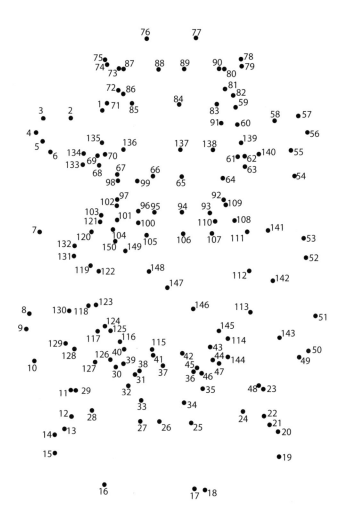

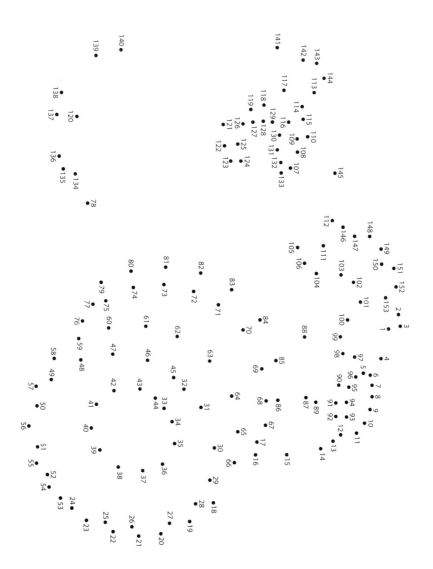

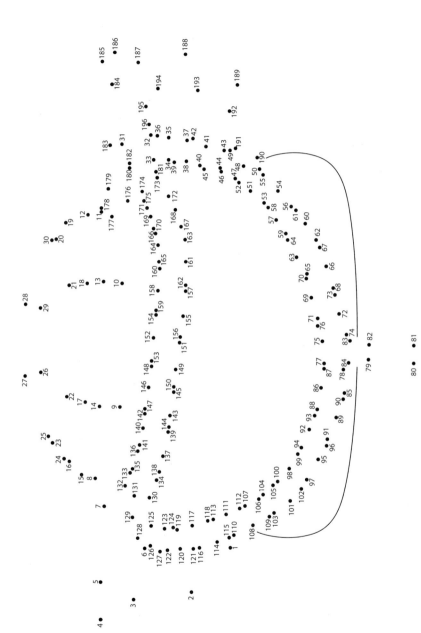

153

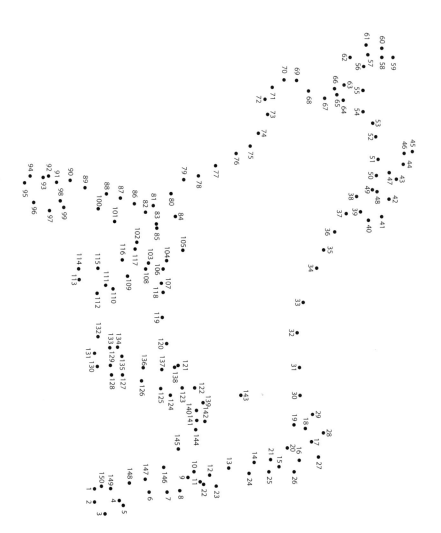

155

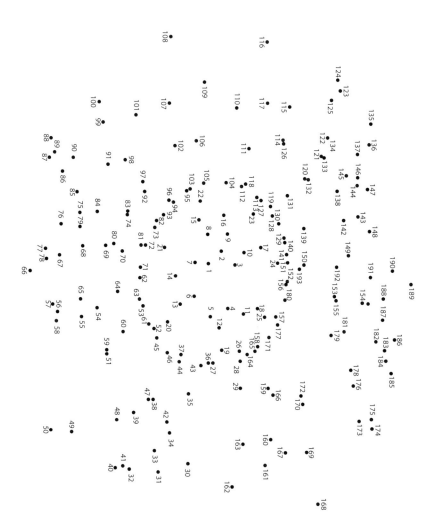

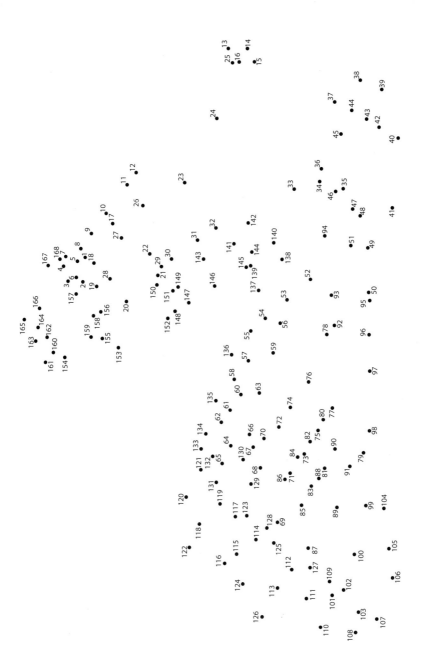

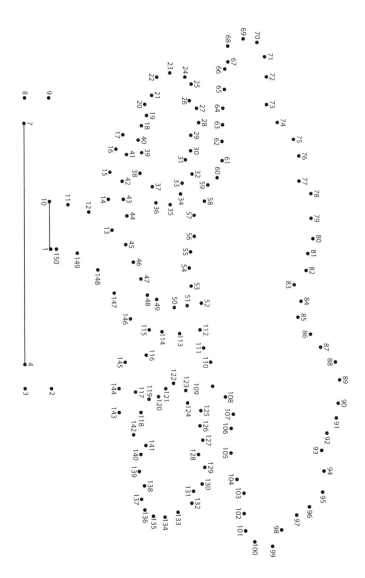

158

List of illustrations